Timothy Jung • M. Claudia tom Dieck
Editors

XR-Metaverse Cases

Business Application of AR, VR, XR and Metaverse

Springer

Editors
Timothy Jung
Manchester Metropolitan University
Manchester, UK

M. Claudia tom Dieck
Manchester Metropolitan University
Manchester, UK

ISSN 2731-4758 ISSN 2731-4766 (electronic)
Business Guides on the Go
ISBN 978-3-031-30565-8 ISBN 978-3-031-30566-5 (eBook)
https://doi.org/10.1007/978-3-031-30566-5

This Springer imprint is published by the registered company Springer Nature Switzerland AG
The registered company address is: Gewerbestrasse 11, 6330 Cham, Switzerland

Preface

Extended reality (XR) technologies including augmented reality (AR), virtual reality (VR), and mixed reality (MR) technologies have already made a huge impact on our business and society especially during the pandemic era. In addition, these immersive technologies have provided a foundation for the recent emerging concept of the metaverse which refers to "an augmented digital world that is blending physical and virtual spaces through the use of XR and artificial intelligence-based systems for users to interact, and/or trade virtual goods or services through cryptocurrencies (e.g. NFTs), with one another and other/virtual entities".

Recently, many interesting and useful applications of XR and metaverse were designed, developed, and applied in the consumer world across different industries but particularly more use cases of the metaverse in the gaming and entertainment and retail industry amongst others. As part of the 7th International XR Conference in Lisbon, April 2022, many interesting use cases of XR and metaverse were presented by industry experts and the result is this book which brings case studies starting with an introduction of each company and the XR or metaverse projects they were involved in. This is followed by a deeper dive into the project which covers feedback from end users and future outlook or roadmap.

We hope you enjoy exploring and learning from the organisations and projects featured in this book.

Manchester, UK

Timothy Jung
M. Claudia tom Dieck

Contents

List of Figures

An Extended Reality Solution for Mitigating the Video Fatigue of Online Meetings

Hello World: Liveness in Virtual Theatre for the Metaverse

Safety Is Everything: Design of an AR·VR Training Simulator for Radiation Emergency Response

List of Table

The Temple of Brunello: Virtual Journeys to Enhance a Unique Product and Its Territory—Brunello di Montalcino Wine

Adele Magnelli, Valeria Pizziol, Roberta Falcone, and Aurelio Destile

1 Company Description

ETT S.p.A. (www.ettsolutions.com) is a digital and creative industry specialised in technological innovation and experience design. It was founded in 2000 and currently employs over 200 people.

The company is a general contractor for experiential installations and complex information systems. From its Genoa headquarters and other venues in main Italian cities and London, ETT is a market leader in concept creation and the management of Italian digital cultural heritage, the design of information systems for smart governance job markets, and integrated smart city systems connecting cities, locations, and people. In order to do so, ETT uses technological innovation to enhance knowledge

A. Magnelli (✉) • V. Pizziol • R. Falcone • A. Destile
ETT S.p.A., Genoa, Italy
e-mail: adele.magnelli@ettsolutions.com; valeria.pizziol@ettsolutions.com; roberta.falcone@ettsolutions.com; aurelio.destile@ettsolutions.com

T. Jung, M. C. tom Dieck (eds.), *XR-Metaverse Cases*, Business Guides on the Go,
https://doi.org/10.1007/978-3-031-30566-5_1

and experience systems. Gathering a wide range of skills in a single production system, ETT integrates innovative solutions in order to deliver specific digital solutions for process efficiency and optimisation. Specialist areas of expertise include tourism, cultural and landscape heritage, training, edutainment, corporate communications, fitting-out of spaces and corners, data management, and data mining.

Regarding cultural heritage solutions, ETT has been active for years in the new media field, in which it creates innovative applications, exploiting the potential of new technologies and combining digital design and advanced storytelling techniques, to create engaging experiences for museums and corporate and public spaces. In this field, since 2008, it has over 3100 multimedia installations for over 1000 museums and private customers, for over 6,5 million visitors.

In the latest years, according to the main developing and emerging trends in new technologies, special attention and research has been paid to create emotional experiences that could develop deeper levels of immersion in virtual spaces and in extended realities via parallel integration of design, storytelling, and cutting-edge technologies. In this scenario, the project Temple of Brunello finds its roots.

2 Project Summary

In order to react to a period of uncertainty, consortiums and producers have had to find a proactive response to the pandemic, implementing innovative virtual and immersive experiences to promote their products and their territories.

In Tuscany, the Temple of Brunello project consists in a multimedia visiting path, both physical and digital, which starts from the narration of a worldwide famous product, Brunello di Montalcino wine, and guides towards a deeper understanding of the Montalcino territory and its history.

In Montalcino, the experience starts in the medieval Saint Augustine complex, an ancient former convent that acts as the starting point of the immersive journey. The Temple of Brunello multimedia set-up was inaugurated in July 2021. The project has been commissioned to ETT by

Opera Laboratori, a leading Italian company in cultural heritage management and has been widely supported by the most important local stakeholders. The project, in fact, has been promoted by the Archdiocese of Siena, Colle di Val d'Elsa, and Montalcino, the Municipality of Montalcino, and the Consortium of Vino Brunello di Montalcino, and is the result of a solid agreement between the institutions and stakeholders involved. These stakeholders, in the difficult period of the pandemic and its aftermath, have worked together to ensure a bright and innovative future for Montalcino and territory.

The museum concept is based on the firm conviction that the wine journey does not end with merely a wine tasting experience, but increasingly represents a cultural phenomenon that can be communicated in an emotional way thanks to innovative and immersive technologies. The multimedia exhibition of the Temple of Brunello aims at promoting and enhancing curiosity towards the Montalcino territory through an experience that, starting with Brunello di Montalcino wine, tells the story of the area over the centuries. The link between the multimedia solutions and the territory is created by describing with the aid of different types of technologies its archaeological and artistic heritage, the landscape, and its precious products. The interactive and multimedia exhibits characterise the interiors of the complex and introduce, with suggestions and memories, the aspects that have made Brunello di Montalcino one of Italy's leading products: its bond with a unique territory, man's commitment and care, the evolution of production processes, stories, and colours of the breath-taking landscape. Brunello di Montalcino wine history is narrated to visitors in an immersive and interactive experience: combining heritage and innovation, the journey culminates with an encounter with the wine that has made Montalcino famous throughout the world, since the end of the nineteenth century.

3 Project Details

The main concept has been to seamlessly integrate physical and digital element, creating an experience that could touch different immersion levels on the *reality–virtuality continuum* (Milgram et al., 1994).

To do so, and to mirror this choice in the physical set-up created, a single narrative thread unites the environments that create the visiting path in the former convent of Saint Augustine. A conceptual and emotional crescendo accompanies the visitor in the discovery of the peculiarities of Brunello di Montalcino wine and the territory in which it is produced, of the work and passion that distinguish the protagonists of its history and its future evolution. Thanks to the narration of the close and constant link with the territory, the visiting experience takes the form of a continuous dialogue between the visitor and the atmospheres that contribute to making Brunello di Montalcino wine so unique, characterised and distinctive.

In the past few years, it has become more and more evident how the boundaries between physical and virtual content within informal learning environments are being blurred, such as cultural and tourism ones, where digital and virtual advances have been adopted as a means to promote engaging and meaningful visitor experiences. Museums and historical sites are gradually learning how best to create highly engaging instructional experiences by emphasising and highlighting particular aspects of an exhibit (Bressler, 2013).

Whilst in the academic field studies that investigate the level of use of extended reality experiences in museums are being carried out (Silva & Teixeira, 2022), it is reliable to assume that extended reality experiences can provide many different benefits in the creation of visiting experiences, for example, the ability to guide the visitors' attention towards aspects that otherwise may be overlooked by or unavailable.

In the Temple of Brunello project, starting from the physical set-up, technology has been integrated in solutions that could bring up intangible aspects of Brunello di Montalcino wine, connected to human led production, still happening today, and the stories and testimonies of the protagonists.

The multimedia itinerary unfolds on the ground floor of the former convent and in its underground spaces is characterised by the combination of various technologies that have been selected to enrich and enhance the naturally characteristic features of the rooms dedicated to the multimedia set-up. In order to create physical technological settings that could not only bring knowledge but also create deeper emotional connections between museum visitors, and more in general tourists, and visiting experiences, one of the multimedia physical set-up examples is an Artwall created with monitors on two side walls and the floor. The monitors are set in a wooden structure that reminds of the roundness of fermentation casks, made out of real wood coming from production barrels donated by local producers (Fig. 1). Other multimedia solutions implemented in the visiting path are project mapping, touch exhibits, and immersive sound design.

Moving along the *reality–virtuality continuum*, the Temple of Brunello visiting path offers different solutions in which components of virtual and real-world environments are integrated, in order to guide the visitor towards immersive and engaging exhibits based on augmented and virtual reality, described in the following paragraphs.

Fig. 1 Artwall set-up in the first underground environment of the visiting path

3.1 InVolo

The visit begins in a covered cloister, an environment that connects the Temple of Brunello with the other two sections of the Civic and Diocesan Museum of Montalcino, the Sacred Art collection and the Archaeological collection, on display in the same building. In the covered cloister area, ten virtual reality stations are set up for the experience called InVolo, which literally translates to *in flight*. The virtual reality experience aims, through an emotional 360° video created with evocative shots and drone flights, to present a first view of the territory that with its unique soil composition and weather allows Brunello di Montalcino wine production.

By wearing virtual reality headsets, visitors can enjoy a spectacular flight over ancient villas and castles, to admire breath-taking views of the city centre, seen from above, and of the small villages in the vast and diverse municipal area. The most modern visual technologies allow an otherwise impossible vision of the typical Montalcino places and panoramas during the different moments of the day, from dusk to dawn, in 13 different locations connected to the main Brunello di Montalcino production cellars and the most evocative views of the area (Fig. 2). With an original soundtrack music to enrich the video, the virtual reality

Fig. 2 Still image from the virtual reality video

experience, strategically placed at the beginning of the visiting path, prepares visitors for discovery and aims to stimulate their curiosity.

3.2 Temple of Brunello: Panoramic Skyline Close to the Wine Shop, Bistrot, and Cafeteria

Moving forward in the visiting path, in an uncovered cloister, the Panoramic Skyline of Montalcino exhibit is the first experience that can be enhanced via a mobile app created for the project. The "L'Oro di Montalcino" mobile app is meant for guiding and expanding the visiting experience: with three proposed itineraries—Saint Augustine Complex, Montalcino, and Territory—it is meant to guide the visit both in the multimedia set-up and in the territory, allowing geolocalisation and presenting points of interest characterised by text, audio, gallery, video and other multimedia contents. Within the physical itinerary, the mobile app makes it possible to activate various contents, favouring interaction between the visitor and the multimedia exhibits, allowing a deeper level of experience customisation. In the uncovered cloister, the interaction between the mobile app and QR Codes presented on the Panoramic Skyline of Montalcino presents 360° spherical photos of the territory. In this way, as well as intriguing visitors by giving them a broad overview of the area's cultural offerings, it allows a virtual and privileged visit to sites and places that are not always open or easily accessible.

The uncovered cloister is also the area that leads to the Wine Shop, the area dedicated to wine tastings and moments of conviviality. The invitation to enter the Wine Shop is related to another augmented reality activated experience: by using their personal device as a remote control, the visitor can take the lead of an interactive window shop. By answering some questions about his or her preferences and feelings, the system will elaborate a profile of the user and animate the interactive showcase with a suggestive video regarding the territory and its beauties, customised on his or her choices.

Furthermore, according to the detected personality, the app will propose a selection of recommended wines produced by local wineries and on sale in the wine shop. By creating an emotional connection between one's own personality and the recommended wine choices, the interaction with the shop window allows it not only to guide the visitor's tasting and purchase experience, but also to connote it as different from what the user may have experienced in similar tourism occasions.

3.3 Augmented and Interactive Shelves in the Wine Shop

Inside the Wine shop, the shelves provide a new interactive experience, offering an in-depth look at four macro-categories of wine. Using the "L'Oro di Montalcino" mobile app, visitors can access additional content and videos that allow them to select and better appreciate the wines on display. These are an integrating part of the store set-up, as they show visitors ever-changing and updatable compositions of images and videos, based on the types of bottles on display and their periodicity. The augmented shelves allow visitors to scan QR Codes (Fig. 3), again using the mobile app, and autonomously access in-depth content.

Fig. 3 QR Code scanning to activate in-depth content

4 Feedback from End Users

As the project was recently inaugurated, analytic information and feedback from end users are not yet available. The most significant data set currently available is the number of downloads of the mobile app, which amounts to 1869 downloads from the Google Play Store and 1461 downloads from the Apple Store.

5 Future Outlook

The Temple of Brunello project can lead to interesting future developments, either to improve the project itself or export it to other contexts. An interesting proposal may lead to the creation of new thematic itineraries, which can further enrich the visiting experience of the city of Montalcino and the surrounding territories. In addition to this, the "L'Oro di Montalcino" mobile app can also be enriched with additional content in augmented reality, providing further insights into the Temple of Brunello.

Thanks to its flexibility and modularity, the project itself can be replicated in further similar contexts, such as other wineries or excellence products both in Italy and abroad.

6 Conclusions

The creation of highly immersive environments, based on the combination of real-and-virtual settings, allows extending visiting experiences and widening the possibilities of fruition and discovery. The construction of virtual and augmented reality experiences allows the implementation of multimedia journeys, where visitors are guided to discover new points of view, in order to understand their multiple implications and facets. As evidenced by the Temple of Brunello project, the integration of extended reality solutions in physical multimedia set-ups can lead to a more complete exploration of an excellence product. The use of multimedia solutions, connected to different areas of the *reality–virtuality continuum*, can guide the creation of deeper emotional engagement in the knowledge of an excellence product like Brunello di Montalcino and the territory where it is born, its history, art, landscape, and traditions. Simply by wearing virtual reality headsets, entering an immersive multi-projection area, or exploring information via a dedicated mobile app, storytelling can be enhanced and enriched in order to create memorable experiences.

References

Bressler, D. M. (2013). Gateways to mobile learning. In Z. L. Berge & L. Muilenburg (Eds.), *Handbook of mobile learning* (pp. 224–234).

Milgram, P., Takemura, H., Utsumi, A., & Kishino, F. (1994, January). *Augmented reality: A class of displays on the reality-virtuality continuum.* Proceedings of SPIE – The International Society for Optical Engineering 2351. https://doi.org/10.1117/12.197321

Silva, M., & Teixeira, L. (2022). eXtended Reality (XR) experiences in museums for cultural heritage: A systematic review. In Z. Lv & H. Song (Eds.), *Intelligent technologies for interactive entertainment. INTETAIN 2021* (Lecture Notes of the Institute for Computer Sciences, Social Informatics and Telecommunications Engineering) (Vol. 429). Springer. https://doi.org/10.1007/978-3-030-99188-3_5

Resuscitation VR: Implementing the Future of Emergency Medicine Training

T. J. Matthews

1 Company Background

i3 Simulations is an immersive technology company that produces augmented reality (AR), virtual reality (VR), and mixed reality (MR) training solutions for the healthcare simulation market. It was spun out of immersive technology incubator AiSolve as an entity focused solely on the healthcare sector and is headquartered in the UK with representation in India, Singapore, and the USA.

The mission statement of i3 Simulations is to democratise learning across healthcare, by designing products for self-guided and peer learning, by flexibility in our business model to outreach underfunded medical institutions, and by supporting content creation and moderation by the subject experts themselves.

T. J. Matthews (✉)
i3 Simulations, Luton, UK
e-mail: tj.matthews@i3simulations.com

T. Jung, M. C. tom Dieck (eds.), *XR-Metaverse Cases*, Business Guides on the Go,
https://doi.org/10.1007/978-3-031-30566-5_2

2 Project Summary

Resuscitation VR (Fig. 1) is aimed at the healthcare simulation sector and targeted towards solving problems that occur in training staff for high-stress, critical care environments. It is aimed at training junior doctors (hereby referred to as "residents") and other clinical staff in critical care units (CCUs) across hospitals internationally. Initially sponsored with Oculus (now Meta) funding programme "VR for Good" (Oculus, 2018) as a pilot study, Resuscitation VR has since been formally launched in 2019 and currently has sign-ups in 70+ organisations in 30+ countries worldwide.

Doctors globally use Resuscitation VR as a compulsory curriculum module to train residents to diagnose and resolve emergency medicine events whilst in a high-pressure, simulated environment. These modules are also utilised for refresher and upskilling training, and alternatives to resource-intensive traditional patient actor or manikin-based simulations.

Resuscitation VR modules are scalable, which means that additional procedures can be designed and developed using the same technological framework—including localisation to international standards, terminologies, and practices. The module library is regularly growing to include more critical care scenarios and localised content supported by this framework, and clinical partners can utilise a co-production design framework for bespoke modules at low cost.

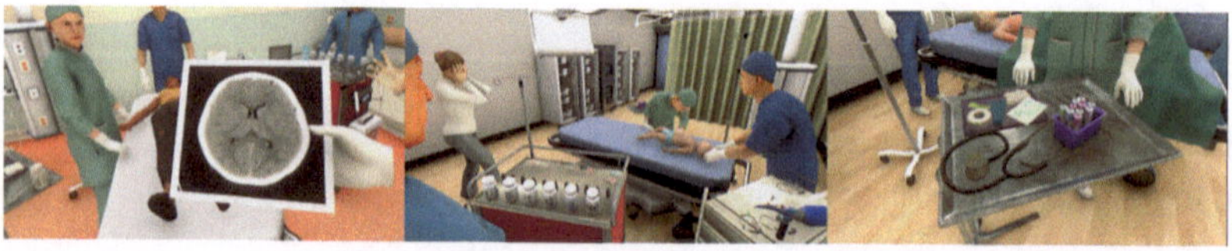

Fig. 1 In-application views of Resuscitation VR

3 Project Details

3.1 Challenge

Resuscitations are high-stakes, low-frequency healthcare events that are frequently and traditionally trained through manikin-based simulations. These scenarios include critical situations ranging from neurological emergencies to cardiopulmonary arrest and are known to be a source of significant mental load.

Much of the stress experienced by a "code lead" physician comes from the need for rapid information processing, situational awareness, and decision-making, rather than in the physical tasks, which are left to other team members.

Due to the high risk of negative patient outcomes, resident physicians are not typically expected to manage resuscitation events, despite a theoretical knowledge of resuscitation procedure—but staffing and circumstance means that they are sometimes placed in this role and responsibility in early clinical practice. Therefore, the first real-life resuscitation event a resident manages is a pivotal career moment that cannot be fully trained for with traditional simulations.

The challenge that critical care units (CCUs) face is giving residents a safe environment that replicates high-stress scenarios and reduces the dependency on manikin-based training, which is expensive and requires the presence of multiple senior medical professionals.

Virtual reality has the capacity to close this gap: to provide a high level of audio-visual immersion and faithfully replicate the real environment, tools, and persons, without the same high resource requirements.

3.2 Solution

Resuscitation VR is split into scenario modules that each focus on a particular type of high-risk patient or emergency. Each module places the user as the "code lead" physician in the room, who must make quick decisions and perform tests to diagnose and stabilise the patient.

The virtual clinical environments are designed to be realistically immersive, not only having the same appearance and layout as a real-world emergency room—originally the genuine resuscitation room at Children's Hospital Los Angeles—but also with an authentic soundscape of hospital noises and alerts.

All scenarios use branched-chain algorithms to alter the virtual patient's physiology beneficially or adversely depending on the user's actions and decisions. Hand-held controllers allow the user to select appropriate physical examinations, treatment options, and staff commands.

As well as offering a safe place to practise, Resuscitation VR also captures rich data—for example, actions, stimuli, decisions—about each user performance, which is then transcribed into personalised scenario feedback and scoring. The primary queries for such feedback are provided by clinical partners during scenario design, but the performance recordings are formatted in such a way to also allow for additional queries to be added via simple filters, including retroactively on past performances.

As the patient and symptoms vary between modules, so too do the medications and tools available, and most crucially, the steps required to revolve the emergency event. Scenarios also have variations, or "difficulties", that challenge the learners to build upon their knowledge and skills to complete the same base scenarios but with additional problems and complications introduced. Beginner modes offer simpler problems and helpful suggestions from staff, whereas in advanced modes the standard protocol may not be effective and the characters around the lead physician will be much more stressed and less patient with mistakes.

Similarly, the Resuscitation VR scenarios offer "distraction" levels, which code the frequency and intensity of external stressors introduced to the learners—for example, evocative language and noise levels. This design caters to strengthening trainees' stress management skills simultaneously with their clinical skills.

3.3 Benefits

This design of engaging learners at the boundaries of their knowledge and skill is the *desirable difficulties* (Bjork & Bjork, 2011) fundamentally found within *deliberate practice* (Anders Ericsson, 2008). Learners engage not with isolated simulation sessions but instead with purposeful and guided training aided both by the escalations within the scenarios themselves and with the specific, targeted feedback for improvement and reflection.

Core learning design behind Resuscitation VR is of experiential learning (Fromm et al., 2021), in which learners get hands-on experience and guided reflections and debriefing on learning. This is the closet virtual equivalent to genuine real-world experience and has high skill transfer and knowledge-retention outcomes.

Additionally, the underlying system design caters for both *self-guided learning* (in which the trainee guides their own learning) and *peer-to-peer learning* (in which trainees guide each other), alongside traditional instructor learning, to increase simulation training frequency and enhance training outcomes (Minocha et al., 2017).

4 Feedback from End Users

Resuscitation VR modules have been validated in multiple studies by doctors and medical staff (Fig. 2).

The first two modules developed for Resuscitation VR are the focus of the subsequent studies referenced in this chapter. These two studies focus on paediatric emergency (infant status epilepticus and paediatric anaphylactic shock) and were developed in collaboration with Children's Hospital Los Angeles. Both scenarios had significant airway, breathing, or circulation problems that matched an emergency severity index (ESI) 1 or 2 resuscitation. After the success of the two paediatric modules, a series of additional paediatric and adult modules were commissioned and produced.

4.1 Initial Pilot

After a published study evaluating the use of Resuscitation VR alongside real-world resuscitation events (Chang et al., 2019), Resuscitation VR

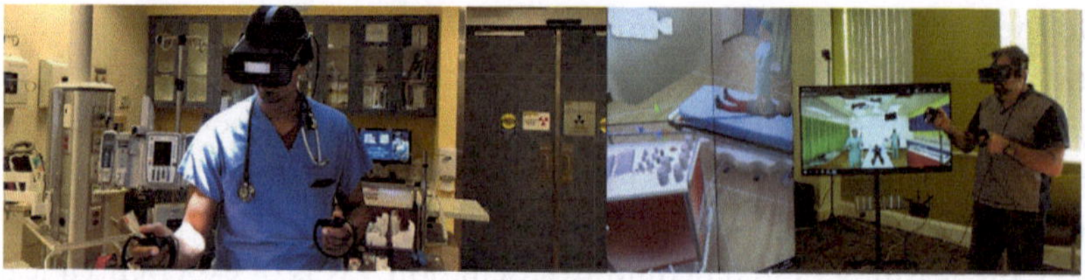

Fig. 2 Resuscitation VR in use

was formally rolled out in April 2019 and has been adopted as a mandatory curriculum material for clinical staff in critical care units (CCUs).

This study found that Resuscitation VR could be most beneficial for residents—in comparison to senior physicians, who had lower stress levels overall across both VR and real-world resuscitations—as early-stage clinicians reached a potential "optimal stress" level whilst using the simulation, which could increase engagement and skill retention.

Doctors have found it to be more cost-effective than manikin-based training which makes it scalable and builds a business case for easy adoption across CCUs. Kathyryn Schaivone, certified simulation educator at Kaiser Permanente Hospital, said, "Currently we are only able to run critical events such as paediatric resuscitation training two to four times per year since we cannot take our teams away from patient care more frequently. VR levels the playing field in a way that doesn't happen with in-person methods and provides the flexibility for more frequent participant in simulation."

Further, "a limitation of many outpatient offices and care centers is lack of space for simulation rooms and simulation centers," explains principal researcher on the project Dr. Josh Sherman, "using Oculus for our VR modules will allow for on-the-spot training without the need for extra real estate."

4.2 Stress Inoculation

These findings were confirmed with a follow-up study (Chang et al., 2020) which similarly found "providing novice learners with simulations that approximate real resuscitations could have potential as stress inoculation" using experiential exposure therapy training concepts.

This study also discussed the value proposition of using VR in simulation centres for training, including "asynchrony—the ability to conduct the simulation any time without a real-time facilitator" and that "VR can provide a suitable complement when physical simulations are less easily transported or delivered".

It also outlined some limitations of standard VR control schemes with seasoned attendings, and novice VR users, which prompted a follow-up study on usability.

4.3 User Experience

To explore this further, a study was conducted on the common user experience in VR healthcare simulations (Matthews et al., 2020), which found a correlation between user errors and novices using a hand-held controller interface, incurring barriers with the *gulf of execution* (Norman, 2013), as well as design considerations for the limited *possibility space* (Bogost, 2008) inherent to virtual simulations.

These findings and recommendations of interaction designs lead into "New Ways to Interact" explored in "Future Outlook".

4.4 Comparison with Manikin-Based Simulation

Finally, a study by Abulfaraj et al. (2021) compared learner performance in the Resuscitation VR simulation vs. high-fidelity manikin-based simulations in a randomised trial.

The study found similar learning outcomes across both the manikin-based control and the Resuscitation VR intervention groups, as well as a high overall satisfaction score showing that it was easy to use and could increase intention to use if available. This finding supports Resuscitation VR as a highly beneficial curriculum tool to supplement traditional simulation training tools and improve simulation training capabilities.

5 Future Outlook

Prompted by these research studies and ongoing needs of clinical partners, there are a number of ongoing innovations being produced for Resuscitation VR.

5.1 New Ways to Interact

Focusing on closing the "*gap of execution*" as outlined in Matthews et al. (2020), hand-tracking controls and intelligent voice recognition systems are being demoed and integrated in all Resuscitation VR modules, to be concluded and launched in 2022.

To support this, a usability thesis is underway to investigate human-centred design advancements for both Resuscitation VR and immersive healthcare simulations in general. It is hoped that this research will strengthen the discipline with standardised design practices and interaction principles.

5.2 New Ways to Build

One identified barrier limiting the wide adoption of immersive simulations is the high technical cost required for new content and scenario customisation (Baniasadi et al., 2020). This is being addressed as part of the Resuscitation VR toolkit in two ways:

Firstly, in partnership with the University of Mississippi Medical Center, an immersive teaching interface is being developed to allow simulation trainers to modify environments, patients, tools, and various other parameters, both in preparation for a simulation training session to meet the learning material, but also live during the simulation session in response to learners' actions and behaviours. This functionality adapts the flexibility of high-fidelity manikin-based simulations and patient actors into the virtual domain.

Secondly, framework development using state-of-the-art AI is underway to allow clinicians and subject experts to design entire modules themselves, without technical knowledge required, using an immersive intuitive interface.

Both of these tools are planned for launch in 2022 and will be formally announced in the coming months.

6 Conclusion

Resuscitation VR is a proven simulation platform for emergency medicine training, implemented in collaboration with medical experts and supported by robust studies. The software can be used to supplement and/or replace traditional manikin-based simulations at a lower upfront and running cost and has the additional benefits of soft skills gain and persistent learning support supported by pedagogy and research.

As the XR ecosystem grows and new possibilities are afforded, so too will Resuscitation VR to meet the training needs of each new cohort of clinicians.

Acknowledgements We thank Dr. Todd Chang and Dr. Josh Sherman for design and research on Resuscitation VR modules, as well as ongoing support. We thank the Emergency and Transport Medicine department and staff of Children's Hospital Los Angeles for support in conducting user trials. This research was supported by the Centre for Digital Entertainment (EP/L016540/1, EPRSC, UK).

References

Abulfaraj, M. M., Jeffers, J. M., Tackett, S., & Chang, T. (2021). Virtual reality vs. high-fidelity mannequin-based simulation: A pilot randomized trial evaluating learner performance. *Cureus, 13*(8). https://doi.org/10.7759/cureus.17091

Anders Ericsson, K. (2008). Deliberate practice and acquisition of expert performance: A general overview. *Academic Emergency Medicine, 15*(11), 988–994. https://doi.org/10.1111/j.1553-2712.2008.00227.x

Baniasadi, T., Ayyoubzadeh, S. M., & Mohammadzadeh, N. (2020). Challenges and practical considerations in applying virtual reality in medical education and treatment. *Oman Medical Journal, 35*(3), e125–e125. https://doi.org/10.5001/omj.2020.43

Bjork, E. L., & Bjork, R. (2011). Making things hard on yourself, but in a good way: Creating desirable difficulties to enhance learning. In *Psychology and the real world* (2nd ed., pp. 59–68).

Bogost, I. (2008). The rhetoric of video games. *The Ecology of Games: Connecting Youth, Games, and Learning,* 117–139. https://doi.org/10.1162/dmal.9780262693646.117

Chang, T. P., Beshay, Y., Hollinger, T., & Sherman, J. M. (2019). Comparisons of stress physiology of providers in real-life resuscitations and virtual reality–simulated resuscitations. *Simulation in Healthcare, 14,* 1. https://doi.org/10.1097/SIH.0000000000000356

Chang, T. P., Hollinger, T., Dolby, T., & Sherman, J. M. (2020). Development and considerations for virtual reality simulations for resuscitation training and stress inoculation. *Simulation in Healthcare, 16*(6), e219–e226. https://doi.org/10.1097/SIH.0000000000000521

Fromm, J., Radianti, J., Wehking, C., Stieglitz, S., Majchrzak, T. A., & vom Brocke, J. (2021). More than experience? – On the unique opportunities of virtual reality to afford a holistic experiential learning cycle. *The Internet and Higher Education, 50,* 100804. https://doi.org/10.1016/j.iheduc.2021.100804

Matthews, T., Tian, F., & Dolby, T. (2020). Interaction design for paediatric emergency VR training. *Virtual Reality & Intelligent Hardware, 2*(4), 330–344. https://doi.org/10.1016/j.vrih.2020.07.006

Minocha, S., Tudor, A.-D., & Tilling, S. (2017). Affordances of mobile virtual reality and their role in learning and teaching. In *The 31st British Human Computer Interaction Conference.* https://doi.org/10.14236/ewic/HCI2017.44

Norman, D. A. (2013). *The design of everyday things.* MIT Press. https://muse.jhu.edu/content/crossref/journals/technology_and_culture/v056/56.3.tenner.html

Oculus. (2018). *Preparing for emergencies before they happen.* https://www.oculus.com/vr-for-good/stories/preparing-for-emergencies-before-they-happen/

A Bridge into the Metaverse: XR-Supported Bridge Inspections

Urs Riedlinger and Leif Oppermann

1 Institute Description

Fraunhofer FIT (Fraunhofer Institute for Applied Information Technology FIT) is an excellent partner for the human-centric design of our digital future. It is 1 of 76 institutes and research units of the Fraunhofer-Gesellschaft, the world's leading applied research organisation. For almost 40 years, Fraunhofer FIT is developing IT solutions tailored to people and seamlessly integrated into business processes. The Department of Cooperation Systems covers three main areas: blockchain and distributed ledger technologies, mixed and augmented reality solutions, and network research. Several research projects along with the "Basic Support for Collaborative Work" (BSCW) groupware system paved the way for more mobile (XR) prototypes beyond the classic

U. Riedlinger (✉) • L. Oppermann
Mixed and Augmented Reality Solutions, Fraunhofer FIT,
Sankt Augustin, Germany
e-mail: urs.riedlinger@fit.fraunhofer.de; leif.oppermann@fit.fraunhofer.de

T. Jung, M. C. tom Dieck (eds.), *XR-Metaverse Cases*, Business Guides on the Go,
https://doi.org/10.1007/978-3-031-30566-5_3

desktop metaphor. FIT's mission is to put research findings and technologies into new perspectives and relations.

With the success of virtual reality (VR) headsets in the gaming sector and smartphones, tablets, and smart glasses suitable for augmented reality (AR), also the interest in such application increases. The Office of Technology Assessment at the German Bundestag published a report on this topic (Kind et al., 2019), including references to the building sector. Besides our expertise for possible applications of smart glasses (Oppermann & Prinz, 2016) and head-mounted displays in German companies (Esser & Oppermann, 2016), preliminary work at our institute on XR for the construction area started with 2004s research project "ARTHUR", a roundtable for architects and urban planners (Broll et al., 2004). Another project in this field was "CoSpaces", focusing on the collaborative aspect for building maintenance and data visualisation (Hinrichs et al., 2008). Furthermore, we compared several mobile cross-media visualisation options in the construction domain (Oppermann et al., 2016). Currently, we are evaluating the application possibilities for 5G using mixed reality and IoT for collaboration support outside the office within our project "IndustrieStadtpark" (https://www.5gtroisdorf.de). Another project "VISION.5G" which focuses on collaboration for building construction and operation started just recently.

2 Project Summary

Bridges are essential for our infrastructure. In Germany, there exist 39,500 bridges within the network of federal roads alone, spanning valleys and rivers, with an overall length of 2100 km. Bridge inspectors must inspect and rate them in regular intervals. According to the existing norms, namely the DIN 1076 (for Germany), they must conduct their inspection with manual labour using manual tools such as hammers and measures. At the end, they must create a report that is handed over to the corresponding owner of the bridge for follow-up tasks. This report contains a detailed description of the assessed damages and a rating (analogue to grades) in several categories. As our infrastructure is ageing and was not designed for the current traffic load, the effort for inspections is found to be increased. Consequently, more effort is needed to support the inspectors for their task.

Information technology (IT) offers multiple support opportunities, and some inspectors are already using ruggedised Windows tablets along with a corresponding software. A web-based version as advancement is currently under development. And Internet of Things (IoT) sensors installed in the field can help to evaluate the bridges' condition.

3 Project Details

Our 1.5-year lasting research project "Structural Inspections using 3D Building Information Models and Augmented/Virtual Reality" on behalf of the German Federal Highway Research Institute aimed at exploring the benefits of XR visualisations together with Building Information Modelling (BIM) data for structural inspections through the example of a box girder prestressed concrete bridge. Together with our partners, namely intecplan Essen (formerly known as "LIST.Digital"), HHVISION, and the Bochum University of Applied Sciences, Fraunhofer FIT developed an MR prototype for in situ usage.

Beforehand, our consortium analysed the state of the art regarding the three main domains: Building Information Modelling, XR technologies, and bridge inspection. We then identified the core process and components needed for a digital structural inspection using work cards and an initial on-site workshop that provided us with an introduction into the field of structural inspections. Then, we started implementing a first AR and a VR prototype. Our main idea was to use AR on site and VR for the preparation and debriefing in the office. We evaluated the AR prototype at a nearby bridge and received an impression of the challenges of the environment, like missing network and GPS coverage inside the box girder and the importance of light for our prototype for orientation. Luckily, the bridge foreseen for our evaluation with domain experts was equipped with light inside. Finally, we evaluated our prototype at a highway bridge in southern Germany with 17 participants from across Germany using a mixed method approach described in more detail in the next section.

Throughout the project, we followed a human-centred iterative approach. As domain experts were involved in our project consortium, we were able to collect early feedback and take design decisions at an early stage with early adopters.

Following the approach from Liebich et al. (2011), saying that BIM is a method, not a software, we saw it as a new way for collaboration and common understanding. In our project we mainly focused on the maintenance of buildings (in that case of structures or even more precise bridges). In Germany, the BIM method is mandatory for public infrastructure projects since 2020 (Federal Ministry of Transport and Digital Infrastructure, 2015); however, it is still in its introduction, e.g., for Federal Highways (Federal Ministry for Digital and Transport, 2021).

Our AR demonstrator comprises three model visualisations: One can either view the virtual model as opaque rendering, or a half-transparent overlay with the option to vary the transparency between 10% and 100% (cf. Fig. 1), or hide the virtual model completely, which was often chosen

Fig. 1 Half-transparent overlay of the bridge from outside (screenshot from our prototype)

to assess the damages and to get a distraction-free view on the surrounding. The bridge inspector may then add a new damage entry with the touch of a button. The damage is localised automatically in the 3D model. Through a form, she or he may then enter more details concerning the damage type. The input form contains a data excerpt from the current state-of-the-art software "SIB-Bauwerke". Bridge inspectors thus can enter the damage according to their known scheme; however, the damage is now assessed in a structured way. Existing damage points are displayed as spheres in the field of view of the tablet. By clicking on such a sphere, the bridge inspector has all the existing information at hand, including a photo and the entire damage history. To capture lengths more easily, we integrated a measuring tool. Existing measures can be captured as a photo and thus associated with a damage (cf. Fig. 2).

Technically, Unity serves us as a visualisation environment. This allows for a common code base between the AR and the VR prototype. The 3D model—originally an IFC file—is imported using the "Filmbox" (.fbx)

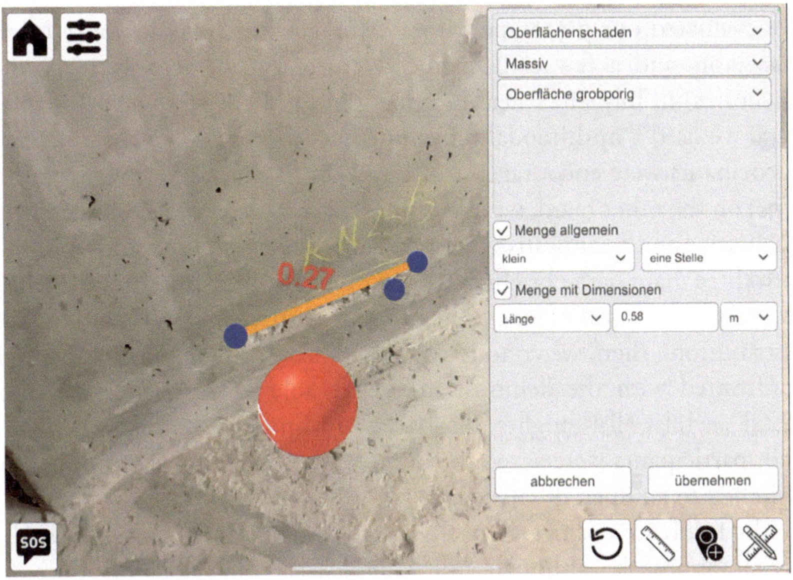

Fig. 2 Damage sphere with measurement tool and input form (screenshot from our prototype)

format. Associated metadata, like information on the employed material, or the manufacturer can be imported using the ".ifc-xml" format. All the damage data is stored in the "BIM Collaboration Format" (.bcf). This separation reduces the amount of data needed to be synchronised, as the geometry and metadata information change less often than the damage data. Regarding localisation, we used image tracking, along with the SLAM capabilities of the employed iPad Pro, with several markers installed in the bridge, as there is no GPS coverage inside the box girder, where most of our user study happened. As soon as the tablet regains Internet connection outside the bridge, our application can synchronise the data to a Common Data Environment (CDE). In our case, we used the "Basic Support for Collaborative Work" (BSCW) groupware system as a CDE. This system is already in use in the administration, and it allows us to connect through a REST interface.

4 Feedback from End Users

We evaluated our prototype with 17 domain experts (a majority bridge inspectors and a few civil engineers currently not actively inspecting structures) in July 2021 near Nürnberg in southern Germany. To collect data, we used a multimodal mixed method approach: On the one hand, participants were encouraged to "think aloud" during testing our prototype; on the other hand, we asked them to complete a questionnaire with qualitative and quantitative questions after their test. Our study was split into three main parts: briefing, workshop, and debriefing. In the briefing, after a short welcome, we clarified the procedure, our goals, and the role distribution. Then, we conducted the workshop where participants were confronted with the demonstrator, were able to experience it, "think aloud", whilst all thoughts, feedback, and findings were logged. At the end, participants were asked to complete the questionnaire and then we switched to an open discussion.

The feedback was overall positive, and we identified a need for such a digital approach, although our demonstrator has lots of room for improvement, especially regarding user interface (UI) improvements.

Nevertheless, all participants agreed on the great potential, even those who appeared to be sceptical at first.

Overall, the participants rated our prototype as "good" with an average value of 2.18 (SD = 1.13) on a German school grade between 1 (very good) and 5 (lacking). All participants tested the core functionalities damage recording and location functionalities, whilst only 13 could test the measure tool for time reasons. The precision of the model overlay was rated as 3.06 (SD = 1.06) and the likelihood of using a digital tool like our prototype for bridge inspections as 4 (SD = 1.22) on a scale from 1 (very poor) to 5 (very good).

One interesting finding was that the damage localisation is precise enough with our approach. Although most of the participants wished to have the ability to move the damage sphere around in space or attach them to a certain surface or building component, they also claimed that an offset of almost half a metre is acceptable to them. It is a huge improvement of the current state of the art of localisation description in the domain, where a "testing direction" is defined and relative positions are roughly captured to the bridge entry or to the segment under investigation (e.g. "20 metres from the start of segment two, on the right side in testing direction, almost waist-high").

5 Outlook

For us as a project team, one lesson learned was that although we had virtual collaboration tools, the in situ workshops cannot be replaced. Despite the Corona pandemic, we found ways to conduct small workshops on site which eased the finding of a common understanding and language and were thus important for the project progress.

Collaboration is also one key aspect that needs further consideration for our prototype. Currently, we synchronise data between the on-site bridge inspector and the office. Often, this would result in asynchronous collaboration. Whilst interruption-free collaboration seems impossible especially inside the bridge due to lacking network coverage, further ways of collaborating outside the bridge should be pursued in the future.

Another topic, the metaverse is currently widely discussed. We believe that our prototype could cover several dimensions presented by Billinghurst (2022), as it offers the possibility to integrate environmental sensors (like IoT sensors) and offers potential also for real-time on-site collaboration. However, we believe that more research is needed apart from the hype and advertisements. Nevertheless, a more widespread use and a higher level of awareness for XR technologies may help to establish systems such as the one presented in the practice in the future. Hence, we see our prototypes as one first step to a potential bridge into a metaverse.

Finally, to bring such systems into practice, further developments of norms and regulations (in Germany: DIN 1076) are required. If the usage of technology-supported is not supported by the organisational framework, it gets difficult or even impossible to use them. We would argue for a human-centred, iterative approach for developing such systems. Like the need of maintenance for our infrastructure, potential digital inspection tools will also need care in the future.

6 Conclusion

Whilst we showed potential with our prototype for a digitally supported structural inspection, we also see room for improvements. Although the feedback from the participants of our user study was positive, the organisational framework needs to be adapted. Further research needs to be conducted to transfer our approach and the found processes to other structures and buildings. This could help to pave the way for a serious application of the metaverse within a work context. We see the trend that IT leaves the office and can be employed in situ using collaborative use cases (Oppermann et al., 2019). Whilst there are technical challenges, we also see great potential for such use cases within the construction industry, not only for the planning and construction but also for the maintenance phase.

Acknowledgements This chapter is based on parts of the research project carried out at the request of the Federal Ministry for Digital and Transport, represented by the Federal Highway Research Institute, under research project No. 15.0666/2019/LRB. The authors are solely responsible for the content.

References

Billinghurst, M. (2022). Delivering the entire metaverse. *Medium*. Accessed May 30, 2022, from https://marknb00.medium.com/delivering-the-entire-metaverse-db4c2afcb6e5

Broll, W., Lindt, I., Ohlenburg, J., et al. (2004). ARTHUR: A collaborative augmented environment for architectural design and urban planning. In *(Proceedings) HC 2004 – Seventh International Conference on Humans and Computers, Tokyo*. Accessed December 6, 2018, from http://discovery.ucl.ac.uk/7853/

Esser, R., & Oppermann, L. (2016). Head-mounted display in German companies – A virtual, augmented and mixed reality check. *i-com Journal of Interactive Media, Special Issue: Smart Glasses, 15*(2), 211–217.

Federal Ministry for Digital and Transport. (2021). *BMDV – Masterplan für die Digitalisierung im Bundesfernstraßen-Bau*. Accessed February 25, 2022, from https://www.bmvi.de/SharedDocs/DE/Artikel/StB/masterplan-bim-bundesfernstrassen.html

Federal Ministry of Transport and Digital Infrastructure. (2015). *Road map for digital design and construction*. Accessed February 24, 2017, from https://www.bmvi.de/SharedDocs/DE/Publikationen/DG/stufenplan-digitales-bauen.pdf?__blob=publicationFile

Hinrichs, E., Bassanino, M., Piddington, C., et al. (2008). *Mobile maintenance workspaces: Solving unforeseen events on construction sites more efficiently*.

Kind, S., Ferdinand, J.-P., Jetzke, T., et al. (2019). *Virtual und Augmented Reality – Status quo, Herausforderungen und zukünftige Entwicklungen*.

Liebich, T., Schweer, C.-S., & Wernik, S. (2011). *Die Auswirkungen von Building Information Modeling (BIM) auf die Leistungsbilder und Vergütungsstruktur für Architekten und Ingenieure sowie auf die Vertragsgestaltung*.

Oppermann, L., Boden, A., Hofmann, B., et al. (2019). Beyond HCI and CSCW: Challenges and useful practices towards a human-centred vision of AI and IA. In *Proceedings of the Halfway to the Future Symposium 2019* (pp. 1–5). Nottingham, UK.

Oppermann, L., & Prinz, W. (2016). Introduction to this Special Issue on Smart Glasses (Editorial). *i-com, 15*, 123–132.

Oppermann, L., Shekow, M., & Bicer, D. (2016). Mobile cross-media visualisations made from building information modelling data. In *Proceedings of the 18th International Conference on Human-Computer Interaction with Mobile Devices and Services Adjunct* (pp. 823–830). ACM.

Enabling the Metaverse with the Development of PopupView: An Augmented Reality Platform

Jessica Symons

J. Symons (✉)
Visioning Lab, Manchester, UK
e-mail: jessica@visioninglab.com

T. Jung, M. C. tom Dieck (eds.), *XR-Metaverse Cases*, Business Guides on the Go,
https://doi.org/10.1007/978-3-031-30566-5_4

1 Company Description

VISIONINGLAB

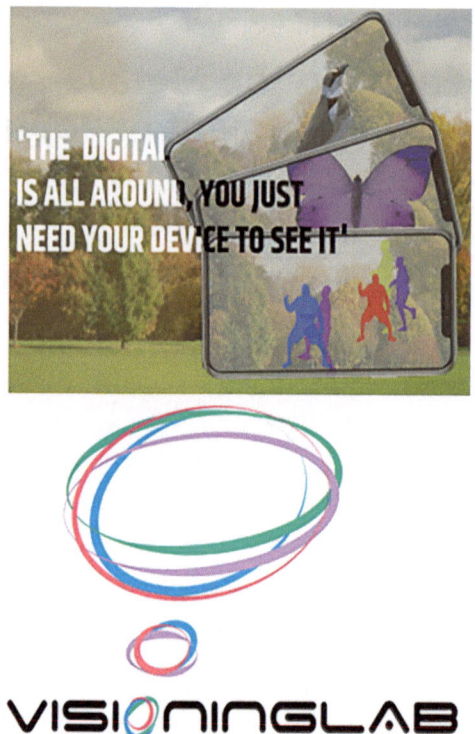

If "Web 3.0 is the world", we want to make sure citizens are engaged in its development.

At Visioning Lab, we take broad ideas and visions for the future and identify emerging concepts and technologies that have game-changing effects on societal structures and environmental challenges. We specialise in the Web 3.0 infrastructure technologies such as augmented and virtual reality, 3D digital worlds, digital placemaking, blockchain, and NFTs. We develop work using the "storyworld" approach, incorporating these technologies and sharing our insights with others.

Our emphasis on placemaking insists that digital data, tools, and technologies should be connected to specific localities. We promote digital placemaking strategies to ensure direction over how civic decision-makers control digital activity in their region's geographical contexts.

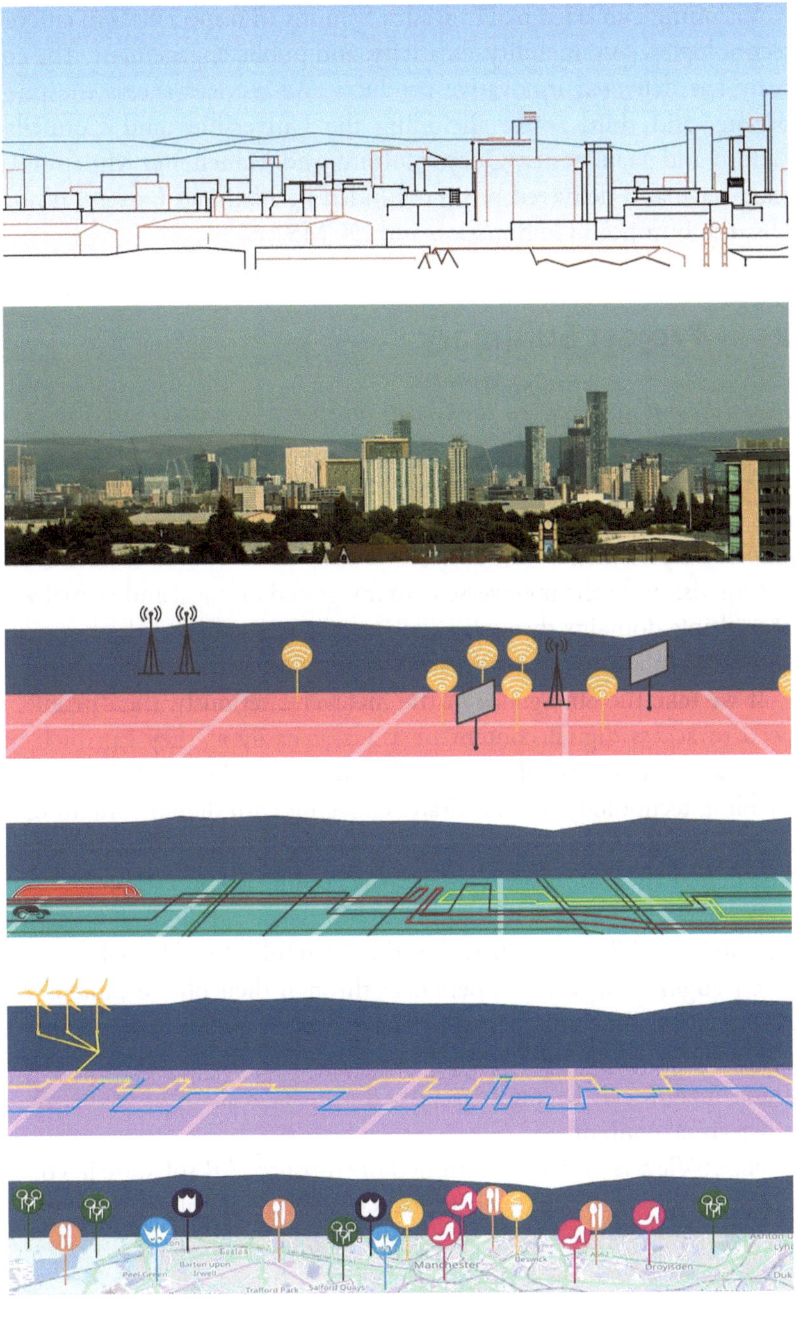
Peel Green
Barton upon Irwell
Trafford Park
Salford Quays
Manchester
Beswick
Droylsden

Visioning Lab is led by Dr. Jessica Symons who specialises in emerging technologies, sustainability, creativity, and public engagement. The company has delivered innovative products and services across the public, private, and third sector including the Universities and Councils of Salford and Manchester, Quays Culture, and Manchester Museum. Our team have also delivered projects funded by National Lottery, Innovate UK, the European Commission and DCMS.

2 Project Summary

PopupView is available on the Google and Apple app stores as a simple, free augmented reality app ready for download onto mobile phones and tablets. Using this app, cultural venues and producers add interest to their content through a "digital" layer, bringing creative and social dimension to their audience experience.

Our vision for the metaverse is an integrated physical and virtual world of multiple domains through which people move freely, whether as digital avatars or as their physical selves in real life.

If we take the emergence of the metaverse seriously, then people will need to access digital content or assets as easily as they can pick up a physical chair or pair of trainers. Augmented reality (AR) becomes the enabling technology that facilitates engaging with digital content on the move. To demonstrate this conceptualisation of AR as providing access to "the digital all around you", we created PopupView in 2019.

PopupView.com, www.popupview.com is an app and an aggregating platform for AR experiences, i.e. the "YouTube for AR" where people access augmented reality experiences through their phone camera much like they use YouTube for seeing short films. The PopupView platform works by using "trigger images" to launch additional digital content. These images can be photographs, drawings, real-world assets, or any other visual content.

PopupView is provided as limited open-source AR software in contrast to proprietary platforms such as Snapchat/Instagram filters and Pokemon

Go/Lightship and bespoke AR apps built by digital design companies for clients such as the National Gallery in London.

The code for the PopupView app and platform is available with permission for download on GitHub and alongside the demonstrator app which contains third-party AR "campaigns" using multiple "trigger" images to show digital content produced in collaboration with artists, writers, and musicians. It is non-proprietary and open-source with permission, available for customisation and collaboration.

3 Project Details

Imagine the following scenario

You are walking down the road when you see the PopupView logo. You recognise that digital assets are available nearby. You tap the side of your glasses and the digital asset materialises. If you want it, you capture it and save to your digital wallet for future use.

PopupView.com is a platform for showing third-party AR experiences just as YouTube shows third-party films. It is a site for providing a "taster" experience of augmented reality using 2D images to "trigger" the display of 2D/3D/animated/audio digital assets. The platform contains over 30 different AR experiences designed by artists, musicians, writers, and producers.

PopupView content is accessed via an app on a phone/tablet. The app uses "trigger" images to show additional digital content in the camera view of the device using "augmented reality" or AR.

Each AR "campaign" on the PopupView platform was developed to share an idea or add interest to an existing offer. For example, at Manchester Museum, we created digital butterflies to emerge from the insect artefacts contained in gallery display cases. For artist Peter Kalu, we used photographs of his artwork to trigger his song about the slave trade.

To develop AR campaigns for the app, Visioning Lab works in collaboration with the campaign "client" to identify images or scenes that could be augmented with additional digital content. These images could be at a physical location such as an art gallery or tourist attraction, or they could be in a book or on a website.

We identify existing digital content or produce additional work as required. This content is incorporated as a campaign into the PopupView platform and so available for viewing through the app. We provide information to the campaign client to incorporate the PopupView app into their marketing material and monitor the downloads and progress of the app use over the campaign period.

We also develop 3D digital content by running workshops for people to make and view their own creative work in public settings. This approach worked well in the Lightwaves PopupView app where digital sketches drawn in virtual reality by visitors to the Immersive Lab in MediaCityUK were exhibited at an art exhibition in Salford Quays. People liked the hand-drawn digital animations by their peers, available as part of an art festival and sharable via social media.

4 Case Studies

One of our most popular AR campaigns is the Birdsong digital experience that helps people recognise birdsong better.

#Birdsong is a digital nature experience for walking trails, visitor centres, museums and galleries and for games and educational packs. The experience is customisable and made available via phones and tablet devices.

#Birdsong works by playing sounds of birds on a device when a user scans a "trigger" image as well as providing information about the bird. The trigger images can be images of the birds, habitats, plants, the natural environment or real-world scenes in the landscape/venue itself.

Groups of People at Lightwaves Festival

Visioning Lab developed an AR app for the Lightwaves Festival using digital drawings sketched in virtual reality by visitors to the Immersive Lab. The work was inspired by LS Lowry and also used photo montages created by fine artist Amber McCormack.

Find the butterflies at the Royal Horticulture Show in Tatton (RHS 2019)
Visioning Lab collaborated with Tatton and Cheshire East Council to animate the Tatton stand at the 2019 Royal Horticulture Show. Artist Jacki Clark made 3D digital sketches using virtual reality. The AR app worked on tablets at the Tatton stand and the butterfly case. Visitors released butterflies by pointing the device camera at the display.

5 Feedback from End Users

User comprehension is the biggest barrier to the adoption of augmented reality. People do not understand what it is, how it works, and its value. In an already saturated media content world, there has been little incentive for people to overcome the learning "hump" necessary to make the cognitive leap required.

Typically people need to work out how to use the app *on their own* after downloading from the app store. Many users will download the app, open it, open a campaign, and select an image. When their device camera opens for them to find that image and "trigger" additional content, they do not know what to do and will often abandon the app at that point. Users rarely recognise the need to point their device camera at a "trigger image", not on their phone but in the world around them. This lack of awareness that the camera can show additional digital content 'triggered' by an image is finally slowly changing through the use of QR codes during the pandemic and filters on Snapchat/Instagram.

Over the past 4 years of working with augmented reality development, audience awareness of "trigger images" was our biggest challenge. To ensure user engagement, we needed to be physically present with a phone or tablet device and an image ready to "trigger" additional digital content. To maximise audience engagement, we would attend events and stand next to the images and invite people to view the AR experience together with us.

For example, referring to the case studies above, at the RHS show in Tatton, we spent 5 days at the Tatton stand with a tablet. The trigger images were photographs of butterflies pinned to a tree sculpture. As people approached the stand, we would say "would you like to see digital butterflies come out of the tree?" or "would you like to wake up the butterflies" which worked particularly well with children. Then we opened the PopupView app on the tablet, hovered the device camera over the photograph of a butterfly, and showed them digital butterflies designed for the art experience as they came into view on the tablet.

Once experienced, augmented reality has a powerful effect on the viewer. Responses are usually very positive with words such as "wow!", "that's amazing", "I love that".

QR codes during COVID helped increase awareness of images as "triggers" accessed through phone cameras. When demonstrating AR campaigns, we can now refer to QR codes and this now produces a positive response and an instant awareness that the phone camera needs to be used and that something happens as a result of hovering over an image.

Once users become aware of the functionality of augmented reality, they adopt it readily. It usually only needs to be explained once and then they will view multiple AR experiences. It was due to this issue around user awareness that we focused on producing PopupView as a platform with very simple AR campaigns where the key feature was using trigger images to "pop up" additional content and we collaborated with artists as the most likely to intrigue audiences and stimulate enough curiosity to work out how to use the app.

6 Future Outlook

The world's leading tech companies are due to launch augmented reality glasses in the next 3 years with Apple Glasses and Snapchat Spectacles in 2023, Meta AR glasses in 2024 and Microsoft, Amazon, and Chinese companies Oppo (Air Glass) and TCL also preparing. The glasses work through a transparent overlay on the lenses and mini speakers built into the sides of the glasses so people can see and hear 2D and 3D animated content in front of their eyes. This industry is projected at $33 billion worldwide by 2027 with AR glasses eventually replacing mobile phones as the main way people access digital content whilst on the move (Statista 2022).

Visioning Lab's augmented reality platform PopupView (www.popupview.com) was designed to take advantage of the emergence of the AR glasses industry. We released PopupView as an app initially, showing 2D/3D animated and audio digital content through mobile phone cameras. We recognised that whilst currently augmented reality experiences are shown through a mobile phone camera, soon the digital view would be through a pair of AR glasses.

To further build the PopupView platform, we need a rich source of "trigger images" with associated digital content (YouTube used sports and music videos to rapidly expand their platform). We have identified the hugely popular graphic novels as a significant source of material for "trigger images" which combined with AR spectacles would create a whole new way of consuming digital content experiences. Our goal is to rapidly produce volume AR experiences using online content such as webtoons as trigger images and audio as digital content. For the millions of webtoon fans worldwide, their platform can offer additional audio and 2D/3D animated content to accompany the existing visuals. We are also always looking for artists, musicians, writers, and producers who want to collaborate in the development of AR experiences.

We are ready to integrate NFTs with the PopupView platform, having recently carried out an R&D project investigating the process. This included a system architecture, review of popular NFT platform APIs, and industry standards for digital assets.

By making PopupView limited open-source, we hope to increase opportunities for co-producing work globally. Interested parties are encouraged to get in touch.

7 Conclusion

Augmented reality is a technology in transition. It needs to be considered in context with the wider digital environment and how this will manifest over the next 10–20 years. It is a critical enabling technology between digital placemaking (where digital assets are placed into context with physical locations) and the metaverse (where digital assets are located in virtual environments).

As a technology in transition however, the process of using augmented reality, particularly with a phone, has not yet become an automatic reflex for the general public. This can be likened to awareness of hyperlinks and the mouse technology when the Internet first came into being over 20 years ago. Back then people were not aware that an underlined blue word on a "page" on a "website" indicated it could be "clicked on" by the round plastic object next to their keyboard (called a "mouse"). Now this process is second nature to people. Indeed, whilst on their phones, people will tap any word on the screen to see if it will take them to additional content.

Similarly, people are beginning to recognise that an image may trigger additional digital information when viewed through a device camera. This awareness increased rapidly during COVID through the use of QR codes for tracking purposes and now widespread use of QR codes for multiple purposes.

The release of AR spectacles by leading international technology companies will further stimulate the takeup and use of augmented reality experiences. Whether or not it will continue to be called "AR" or "augmented reality" however is unlikely. New terminology will emerge that is better suited to the devices used. We predict that the use of "HUD" or "Head-Up Display" is likely to transition across when the use of AR glasses becomes more mainstream.

"A head-up display, or heads-up display also known as a HUD is any transparent display that presents data without requiring users to look away from their usual viewpoints." (Wikipedia)

An Extended Reality Solution for Mitigating the Video Fatigue of Online Meetings

Cornelius Glackin, Nigel Cannings, Vigneswaran Poobalasingam, Julie Wall, Saeed Sharif, and Mansour Moniri

1 Company Description

Intelligent Voice is a global leader in the development of proactive compliance and eDiscovery technology solutions for voice, video, mixed reality (MR), and other media. The core business of the company is speech recognition and natural language processing technology, providing complex analytic capabilities of speech audio. Its clients include government agencies, banks, securities firms, contact centres, litigation support providers, international consultancy, advisory businesses, and insurers, all involved in the management of risk and meeting of multi-jurisdictional regulation. Fundamental to its success, its patent-pending and patented technologies are developed by a team of dedicated researchers and system

C. Glackin (✉) • N. Cannings • V. Poobalasingam
Intelligent Voice, London, UK
e-mail: neil.glackin@intelligentvoice.com

J. Wall • S. Sharif • M. Moniri
University of East London, London, UK

T. Jung, M. C. tom Dieck (eds.), *XR-Metaverse Cases*, Business Guides on the Go,
https://doi.org/10.1007/978-3-031-30566-5_5

engineers based in the UK. The company leads the market and maintains its strengths in the areas of thought leadership, innovation, R&D, and providing solutions to its clients.

This project was supported by an Innovate UK Knowledge Transfer Partnership (KTP) in collaboration with the University of East London (UEL). UEL provided expertise in virtual reality (VR), augmented reality (AR), 3D tele-immersion, video processing, animation and personalisation of avatars, and audio adaptation and reconstruction.

2 Project Summary

COVID-19 and the related global lockdowns meant online meetings were no longer just an option (Richter, 2020). This new normal was necessitated by a movement from synchronous in-person meetings to synchronous online meetings (Davison, 2020). Post-pandemic, there has been a permanent shift towards this online communication (Guyot & Sawhill, 2020). However, the new normal has seen the rise of a new phenomenon, "Zoom fatigue", also known as video fatigue (Fosslien & Duffy, 2020). This is due to the lack of naturalistic cues being shared in the current tele-conferencing technology, together with the feeling of being observed all the time. During in-person communication, participants follow the 7-38-55 rule to decipher the meaning behind what's being said; 7% verbal, 38% tone of voice, and 55% body language (Mehrabian & Wiener, 1967). Video calls take away most body language cues, but because the person is still visible, the brain still tries to compute that non-verbal language. It means that participants are working harder, trying to achieve the impossible. This impacts data retention and can lead to participants feeling unnecessarily tired.

At the least, part of the answer could lie in the growing world of VR gaming, where the action is driven by the user's actions, usually through a gamepad or keyboard. The visual representation of the person is an avatar. This allows the human operator to have a degree of distance from their online presence. So, if they need to scratch their nose, the avatar is not mimicking them. On a video call, all actions are immediately transmitted and seen by other participants and that puts extra pressure on everyone involved. But of course, participants in online meetings interact differently to gamers and, hence, will need a different type of control. This is where the voice becomes so important.

To avoid unnecessary user actions, it is desired to be able to turn off the camera completely. The actions of the avatars need to be driven by what the user is saying. The speech and emotion recognition expertise of the project partners allow understanding of what is being said, and how it is being said (Iyer et al., 2022). If the tone is light and friendly, the avatar will relax and smile. If the tone is aggressive, it may lean forwards to make a point. Virtual participants can sit naturally in a conference room or sit on the deck of a yacht to sip cocktails. The setting is irrelevant. The point is that it simplifies the information that the brain needs to compute, preventing "Zoom fatigue". Additionally, moving away from standard video conferencing reduces the bandwidth requirements of the application.

This project transformed the way online meetings happen enabling virtual shared experiences with cutting-edge AR/VR technology, speech-to-text and emotion recognition technologies, and sub-real-time hardware acceleration using high-performance computing (Ali et al., 2019).

3 Project Details

The technology presented here, called iVXR, uses both the Android and iOS developer kits to build an immersive meeting experience (see Fig. 1). The product can support each one of the following modes: *3D Mono*, standard 3D rendering in a standard display, supported by Windows 11, Windows 10, Android (version 7.0 or above with ARM64 architecture), macOS, and iOS (including iPadOS); *3D Stereo*, also known as Virtual Reality (VR) on the Oculus Quest 2; *AR Mono*, AR rendering in a standard display, supported by Android with ARCore support and iOS (including iPadOS) with ARKit support; and *MR Stereo*, "Passthrough" mode on the Oculus Quest 2 and HoloLens 2. The technology also supports the inexpensive cardboard options with split screen stereo AR or VR options. The cross-platform multi-mode functionality ensures that meetings can be conducted with any combination of application modes for the participants.

Fig. 1 AR Mono application mode, where the computer-generated imagery (CGI) is augmented onto the actual real-world video stream and rendered in a standard display

Fig. 2 iVXR UI, providing authentication and a configurable 3D avatar system shown in portrait and landscape view on a smartphone (iPhone)

This project utilises the Unity game engine as the basis of the application and user interface (UI) (see Fig. 2), a proven solution for massively multi-user applications, and this together with the preferred inexpensive

MR technology is intended to provide a useful application for a wider community of potential users (http://unity3d.com). The user's avatar can be configured and personalised using authentication supported by Google Firebase and is also stored locally in their profile (https://firebase.google.com/).

The application offers fine-grained personalisation of the avatars, around appearance, gender, ethnicity, and clothing. Avatars are animated in real time. Their facial expression system is based on the Facial Action Coding System (FACS) (Farnsworth, 2019) (see Fig. 3), providing eye movements of blinking, narrowing, open and closing, squinting, up and down, and left and right. Facial emotions include neutral, happy, sad, surprise, fear, anger, disgust, and contempt. The head can turn left to right, up, and down, and tilts forward and back. Avatar bodies and fingers are animated using an animation sequence clip system. Real-time communication of avatar movements across meeting participants in the shared experience is implemented using a third-party application

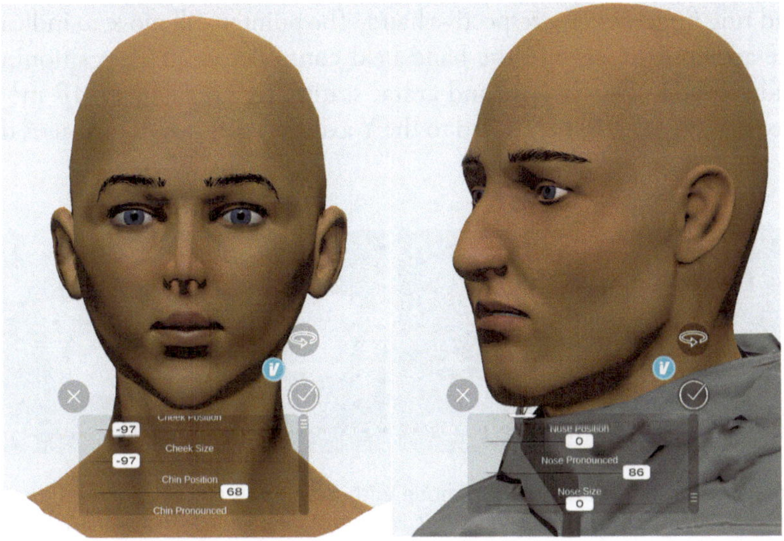

Fig. 3 Avatar facial geometry customisation options, up to 255[30], also supporting male/female genders, 35 skin colours, 6 hairstyles with 22 different hair colours, 20 eye colours, and a limited selection of clothing and shoe colours

programming interface (API) called VIVOX, a subsidiary of Unity Technologies (https://unity.com/products/vivox).

The application provides near real-time subtitling of the speech audio using the company's Automatic Speech Recognition (ASR) engine, which employs NVIDIA's Riva deep learning framework (https://developer.nvidia.com/riva), which serves the streaming ASR models, and a GStreamer bridge to the Unity-based application (https://gstreamer.freedesktop.org/), as shown in Fig. 1. The incorporated ASR technology was benchmarked on the company's proprietary speech test corpus, achieving an accuracy of correct words at 97.4% and a word error rate (WER) of 5%. Speaker-separated Smart Transcripts are produced by iVXR and automatically emailed, copied, or saved after each meeting, serving as a permanent record (Glackin et al., 2019). Real-time audio and chat communication are supported by VIVOX.

For the headset devices, Oculus Quest 2 and Hololens 2, hand tracking is in operation to interact with the UI, enabling the user to control the environment without hand-held controllers in VR and MR modes (see Fig. 4). Users switch the controlling hand by pinching the thumb and ring fingers on the respective hand. The pointer will move to indicate the active hand, as with the hand-held controller. Scaling, positioning, and rotation of the avatars and avatar seating are available in MR mode (see Fig. 5). Rotation is limited to the Y-axis, whereas positioning uses the

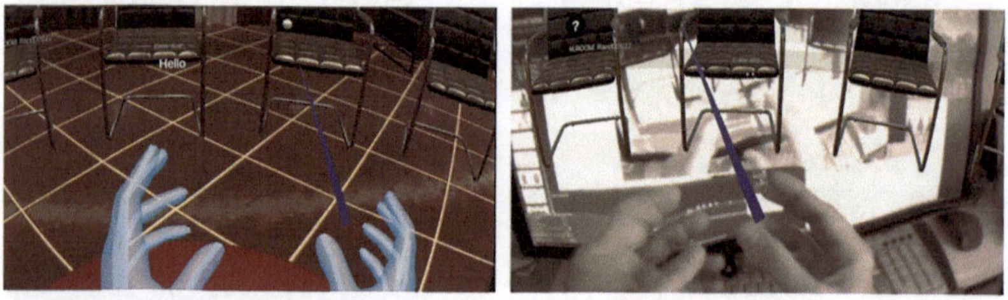

Fig. 4 Left: Hand tracking in VR mode with the Oculus Quest 2. Here, the right hand has the pointer, which means it is controlling, active, or dominant. Right: Hand tracking in MR mode with the Oculus Quest 2. Here, the camera feed of the actual hands are visible, and the right hand has the pointer, which means it is controlling, active, or dominant. This is a render buffer capture using SideQuest software

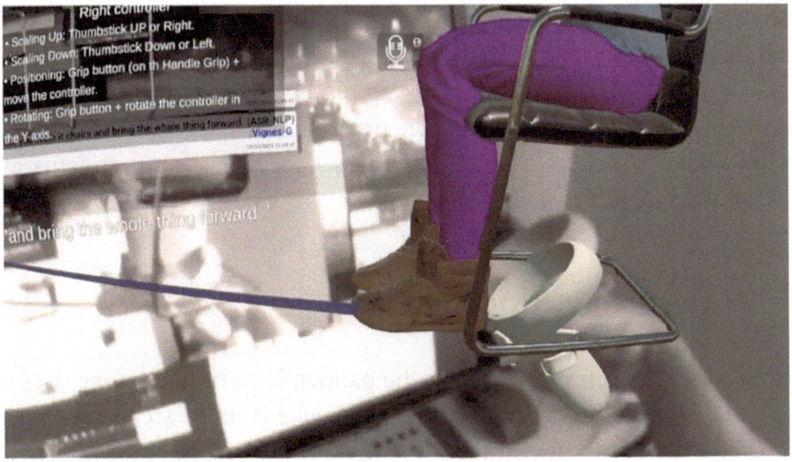

Fig. 5 In MR mode, the user's avatar and chairs are scaled, positioned, and rotated in the Y-axis next to the computer screen. Positioning and rotation are done using the hand-held controller's position and rotation. In this case, the right-hand controller is visible in the background. It is possible to observe that the hand is bending to rotate the controller for avatar and chair rotation in the Y-axis. This is a render buffer capture using SideQuest software

entire 3D space. The user's avatar and chair placement initialise on the top of the 3D overlaid controller.

4 Feedback from End Users

Regular user testing sessions have taken place amongst the project partner's staff to elicit feedback on and to support iterative refinement of the application. In terms of usability and user experience, the workshops focused on the ability of the users to join the meeting from the various supported platforms; ease of personalisation of the avatar and configuration of the virtual environment; technical feedback on latency, responsiveness, sound quality, and transcription accuracy; and the naturalness of the shared experience. Our users have expressed high levels of satisfaction, whilst identification of practical issues around usability have informed ongoing development, whilst feedback on user experience has indicated positive responses to feelings of engagement with iVXR's virtual environment. Increasingly more productive meetings amongst the project partners using iVXR are taking place, reflecting the improvement through this ongoing consultation process. A broader user study is in preparation, to collect more specified user feedback from students and staff at the University of East London.

5 Future Outlook

Attempts have been made during the pandemic to try to change the current 2D imagery of video meetings and make it more accessible. Teams "Together" mode is an example. But these endeavours do not resolve the underlying problems of "presence". There are numerous competing solutions in various stages of development in the marketplace, such as Spatial, Horizon Workrooms, MeetinVR, Glue, Mozilla Hubs, BigScreen, ENGAGE, Rumii, AltspaceVR, Rec Room, and FrameVR. However, it is difficult to separate the conceptual from the real implementations.

In this project, the focus has been on providing an immersive meeting experience, with reduced bandwidth by concentrating on the audio channel, cross-platform support, speech and emotion recognition, and natural language processing technology. Building on the company's patented privacy preserving technology for audio communication, the ongoing plans for this solution are to support secure communication, making iVXR a security-conscious technology that integrates with the daily business workflow. The company is also investigating other use cases for this technology, such as VR for education and telemedicine.

6 Conclusion

This chapter presented a summary of the efforts and technological enhancements that we have made in order to address the phenomenon of video fatigue. The presented technology is audio-based solution for immersive online meetings, which reduces communication bandwidth and provides an interactive, portable, searchable, and speaker-separated transcript of the meeting. Inexpensive technologies like the Oculus Quest 2 provide a vehicle for this application to reach a wider audience. As more AR applications become available for the end user, the hardware to support these will continue to reduce in price and become increasingly accessible. Having started this project pre-pandemic, the application described here is timely and provides a viable alternative approach to standard videoconferencing, promoting more effective and efficient meetings.

Acknowledgements This work was supported by an Innovate UK Knowledge Transfer Partnership (KTP) Grant No. 011056.

References

Ali, A., Glackin, C., Cannings, N., Wall, J., Sharif, S., & Moniri, M. (2019). A framework for augmented reality based shared experiences. *Immersive Learning Research Network-iLRN.*

BigScreen. https://www.bigscreenvr.com/

Davison, R. M. (2020). The transformative potential of disruptions: A viewpoint. *International Journal of Information Management, 55*, 102149.

Engage. https://engagevr.io/

Facebook Technologies, LLC. "Meta Quest Workrooms." https://www.oculus.com/workrooms/

Farnsworth, B. (2019). *Facial Action Coding System (FACS)—A visual guidebook*. Boston.

Fosslien, L., & Duffy, M. W. (2020). How to combat zoom fatigue. *Harvard Business Review, 29.*

Frame. https://framevr.io/

Glackin, C., Dugan, N., Cannings, N., & Wall, J. (2019, September). Smart Transcription. In *Proceedings of the 31st European Conference on Cognitive Ergonomics* (pp. 134–137).

Glue. https://glue.work/

Google Firebase. https://firebase.google.com/

GStreamer. https://gstreamer.freedesktop.org/

Guyot, K., & Sawhill, I. V. (2020). *Telecommuting will likely continue long after the pandemic*. The Brookings Institution.

Hubs, Mozilla. https://hubs.mozilla.com/

Iyer, S., Glackin, C., Cannings, N., Veneziano, V., & Sun, Y. (2022). A comparison between convolutional and transformer architectures for speech emotion recognition. In *IEEE International Joint Conference on Neural Network Proceedings*. IEEE.

MeetinVR. https://www.meetinvr.com/

Mehrabian, A., & Wiener, M. (1967). Decoding of inconsistent communications. *Journal of Personality and Social Psychology, 6*(1), 109.2.

Microsoft inc, AltspaceVR. https://altvr.com/

Microsoft Teams Together Mode. https://techcommunity.microsoft.com/t5/microsoft-teams/enabling-together-mode-in-ms-teams/m-p/1698285

NVIDIA Riva. https://developer.nvidia.com/riva

Rec Room. https://rec.net/

Richter, A. (2020). Locked-down digital work. *International Journal of Information Management, 55*, 102157.

Spatial Systems. https://spatial.io/

Unity. http://unity3d.com

Vivox. https://unity.com/products/vivox

Hello World: Liveness in Virtual Theatre for the Metaverse

James Simpson

1 What Do Audiences Want?

1.1 Context

The live events industry, particularly theatre, sometimes has connotations of being low-tech and often only for the elite. Theatre may be one of the oldest industries in the world, but it has endured because it has remained technologically up to date. Today, it is a far less wealthy industry than it was in the nineteenth century, which means that a lot of technology is borrowed from other industries and reinvented to serve the purpose of entertaining audiences.

To take an early example, Wolfgang Mozart wrote the Magic Flute in response to a recent technological development: pyrotechnics. He chose to write into his story a trial by fire and a trial by water, which would use red and blue flares to create coloured light on stage. In a time when all

J. Simpson (✉)
Copper Candle, London, UK
e-mail: james@coppercandle.co.uk

T. Jung, M. C. tom Dieck (eds.), *XR-Metaverse Cases*, Business Guides on the Go,
https://doi.org/10.1007/978-3-031-30566-5_6

light was produced by candles, this effect on stage would have seemed incredible and innovative to audiences of the time.

Today, the opera industry is amongst the most technically demanding workspaces in any industry as it manages to combine automation, digital video, sound, live filming, and digital manufacturing into its production practices. Theatre has a culture of engaging with new technologies to create spectacular experiences for audiences.

1.2 Virtual Theatre

The emergence of virtual theatre was gradual pre-pandemic, as innovations were led by funded venues. Meanwhile, the Audience of the Future programme, funded by Innovate UK, led to several new use cases being created, including the RSCs plans for a mixed reality, location-based experience of *Midsummer Nights Dream* by William Shakespeare. This was cancelled due to the pandemic and replaced with a remote experience viewed on a web browser as one of many solutions to pandemic theatre.

The pandemic certainly acted as a catalyst for virtual theatre as physical presentation had to be paused. An industry which runs a hand-to-mouth business model couldn't afford to risk producing works which may get cancelled in the future, and so they turned to virtual theatre models and digital streaming to keep audiences engaged with their brands.

Copper Candle has been proactive in developing use cases and working with theatres to find ways of meeting different audiences' expectations in each scenario. The problem facing the creation of virtual theatre is that it hasn't benefited from generations of development to discover what works and what doesn't. This emerging sector is in its infancy, as the cinema industry was in the early twentieth century. In that time, cinema created an experience that remediates the theatre industry with an auditoria set-up, theatrical onboarding, and in the very early days of cinema, a format of presentation which included a presenter standing in front of theatrical curtains.

Remediation is an important part of emerging entertainment industries, as we try to use what we already know to start a new industry. However, the virtual theatre sector is as much games as it is theatre, and remediation of this new format using only theatrical knowledge is weakening our potential to develop this new sector. The RSC correctly brought in teams of experts from across games, film, immersive theatre, and Shakespearian theatre to develop *The Dream* to ensure it created a product that remediated content that was appropriate to the new format.

The inconvenient truth is that we don't yet know how to make this content because we don't yet know our audience as it is still emerging. We have game enthusiasts watching concerts in Fortnite, traditional theatre attendees watching digital live streams using cameras, and now audiences being introduced to virtual reality and the metaverse.

1.3 The Value of Liveness

This project was funded by Innovate UK under the Audience of the Future programme (Design Foundations Round 2). It posed the question, *what do audiences want?* And Copper Candle proposed to discover what audiences want from liveness in virtual theatre.

The reason this question is important for Copper Candle is because of its investment made in live streaming technologies which allow the sharing of motion capture, audio, and theatre lighting control data via cloud servers to reach remote users anywhere in the world. These investments are costly and are based on the assumption that live theatre in a virtual word *must* include live performance.

This assumption was brought into question when the producer of a prior project decided to create a screen recording of the real-time game view which was being broadcast as a screenshare to remote participants. This screen recording would be used as a backup in case the technology failed during a live performance and could be switched to the recording to ensure continuity for the audience which is a practice used regularly on live events and broadcasts where a particular effect is high risk and very noticeable. Key moments of the Olympics are pre-recorded for instance and held on standby during a live broadcast in case of a failure during the live display.

When the producer at Copper Candle proposed that an edited, high-quality capture was produced which went beyond the capabilities of the standard live presentation, it undermined all of the work being done to create live streaming tools. The point was raised that the audience wouldn't notice the difference either way, because the end product looks the same.

From this emerged the research question: would an audience notice if we modified their experience to use high-quality, pre-recorded content to replace the live they are expecting? Will the audience engage with the experience more because it is live and how would they interact with each other? The assumption at the start was that audiences experience liveness because the moment is shared with others and that they wouldn't notice the difference between live content and recorded content in most situations.

2 The Projects Methodology

2.1 Research Mechanics

The mechanisms in place to discover this covered two methods. First was a survey for participants after the experience which looked at their emotional responses. Second was a system built into the application itself that measured a subliminal response from the audience, turning the game application itself into a data collection tool which measured button clicks and interactions. There were 100 participants in this experiment over 27 performances, ranging from 15 in some shows to only 1 in others. A total of 57 participants responded to the survey. The survey participants were from a mixed demographic of ages, locations across the UK (some international), and an equal gender split as well as an equal number of regular game and theatre participants.

2.1.1 Survey

The survey needed to create a baseline set of answers which asked the audience to identify their connectedness to the performer, the other audience, and the story. It focused on key parts of the story which asked questions such as how important it was for the moment to be experienced live? The moments in the show it identifies, such as the dance or a particular section of dialogue, were in reality a mixture of live and pre-recorded content, sometimes with one performer switching to pre-recorded content whilst the other continued to be live. At this point, the participant isn't aware that the performance contains any pre-recording at all; they assume it is all live because it has a scheduled start time and the performers use direct address to them at the start, so the answers are supposed to test whether the pre-recorded responses are different to the live sections' responses.

Later in the survey, it is revealed that sections of the experience are pre-recorded and the baseline responses are then compared to the new answers. This allowed the responses to reveal if an awareness of liveness is important by knowing if the audience who were unaware that their experience was "fake" and if they were in any way removed from the experience emotionally compared to those who did realise.

The survey also allowed more technical questions to be asked to understand their enjoyment of voting systems in the experience, their connection to the audience, and what mechanisms in the experience made that work (Fig. 1).

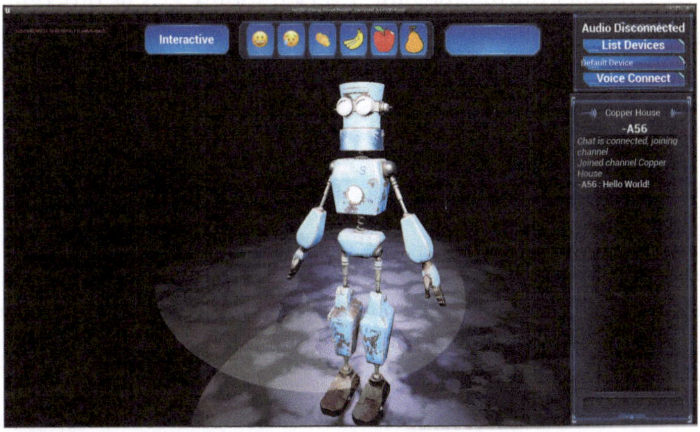

Fig. 1 Hello World application including admin log windows

2.1.2 Data Tracking in Game

Surveys can sometimes reveal an intentional response and not the instinctual choice. To measure the real-life situation, the game application, built in Unreal Engine, was able to track each button interaction and print it to a log file held on an admin server accessible only to the principal investigator. This print log contains a record of special interactions listed below.

2.1.2.1 Directors View/Interaction Mode

The audience had the ability to switch between a mode which creates a pawn actor and allows them to navigate the scene as they would in a computer game, and to a camera output which is controlled live via the live streamed lighting desk data. Each time the buttons were clicked it printed to the log which user and at what time they decided to switch views.

2.1.2.2 Chat Window

A chat window allowed the audience to talk to each other and the performers, where they could respond directly to the performers' direct address to them, to vote or make suggestions on the narrative, or to talk with each other during the plot. Every response was recorded in the print log too.

2.1.2.3 Emoji Buttons

A key research mechanism was the use of buttons to create responses from the audience to the game application. This included applause, laughter, and a set of fruit which could be pressed to send responses to votes. When pressed, the audience would see an instant reaction on their screen of the emoji spinning in their window and disappearing into the scene, creating a visceral interaction.

These buttons were deliberately not connected to the rest of the experience, creating no interaction at all with the rest of the audience, the story, or the performers. The test was to see whether the audience would use these buttons for their own gratification and if they would notice that it had no impact on the storyline. The button clicks were also printed to the log file, so there was a record of the audience's intention to use the buttons. The ability to view voting responses became part of the production as a way to test audience's engagement with real voting instead of votes that created a pre-determined response.

2.2 Equipment and Processes

The production was presented as a 15-min, two-hander performance (two actors on stage together) which incorporated live interaction with the audience as well as dance and special visual effects. Every part of the production had the ability to run live and the only reason not to run some of it live was because of the choices to build in research mechanisms to test different audience responses to live and pre-recorded content.

Key to this system is a plugin for Unreal Engine which has been developed by Copper Candle to allow parametric control of game applications using a theatrical lighting control system. These control interfaces are designed to allow operators fast and efficient manipulation of thousands of parameters of data via nested pallets of pre-configured positions and looks. A good lighting operator can control a live music events lighting in a very similar way to a musician playing a keyboard. This plugin allows for this powerful interface to be integrated into Unreal Engine to provide the same parametric control of anything from lights, audio, objects, positions, and game mechanics within Unreal's visual scripting system, blueprints.

Copper Candle's other products, *Copper Stream* and *Bone Stream,* allow for low-latency communication between the source data (lighting desks and motion capture, respectively) to the game application via a remote cloud server on AWS. Using these combined methods, it is possible to iteratively control live content on the published application whilst working with a theatrical design process familiar to existing practitioners. This meant that the director and performers didn't need to adapt their process to create content, they could observe their established language and communication tools and had familiarity with the performance protocols used by stage managers and operators of live performance. They do, however, still need to consider the design for the medium, to ensure that they are providing an experience that works for audiences of virtual theatre instead of traditional theatre audiences.

The performers wore perception neuron (PN3) suits made by Noitom. These use inertial sensors to detect movement and create a relatively accurate skeleton rig which was reliable enough for a research activity. For live performance, an optical motion capture system would have been more accurate and reliable, but the PN3 suits provided the advantage of flexibility so that more work could be undertaken without requiring access to an expensive studio during several weeks of R&D and design iterations.

2.3 Story

The general story is set in the metaverse, with an AI represented as a robot discovering themselves and their relationship to human beings. The protagonist is a Scottish woman who has joined the metaverse for the first time and has personified herself as a robot. There is light humour as the combination of Scottish and American accents get confused with the language. We relate to the humans' frustration with their AI, just as many do in real life, but with the added twist that the AI is now personified as a performed avatar, and we can tell from the body language that these mistakes are often intentional and motivated by their own amusement.

3 Discoveries

The two research mechanisms used, the survey and the data tracking, created related and complementary findings that supported each other. More than 60% of the audience were not aware that they were watching pre-recorded content at any point in the show and the majority were not aware that their voting choices were often ignored.

Most audience members were content with finding out their experience wasn't genuine once they recognised that pre-recorded content resulted in higher quality content. The fact that motion capture data might not be coming from a live performer was not a requirement, but it enhanced the audience interaction when the responses were live.

The audience felt that they connected better to the performer in this virtual theatre experience than they would in a traditional theatre experience, mainly because they were able to communicate and interact with the performer which most traditional theatre experiences don't allow. They felt even more connected to the other audience members than they did to the performers which was seen as a good thing.

The voting options were a very popular component of the experience with audiences enjoying the ability to choose the narrative and influence the show. Even when they found out that some of their voting choices were ignored, they didn't mind because it was more interesting for them to see what other audience members were saying in the chat as it increased a sense of togetherness for them.

The print log of interactions showed that audience members would try to reinforce their vote by clicking multiple times. Most users pressed the button more than once which they might have done because of how this might look at the receiving side of the voting system, and how it might inspire or motivate the performer, unaware that the performer didn't see any voting responses.

The applause and laughter buttons were also clicked on regularly but only at points of interaction with the audience. If something funny happened in the show, the audience were less likely to click an emoji icon than if they were called out by name or as a conclusion to a voting sequence. This suggests that the audience adopts a passive viewing experience when they are not being engaged with by the performer. Their interaction with the application and user interface only happens when an activity demands pro-activity.

The takeaway for better work in the future is to ensure that all development work happens in the medium and not in the physical world. This means engaging with motion capture early, building early versions of the set design in the virtual world and performing within it. Regular testing with audiences is also essential to judge their interaction and purpose within the narrative. Not doing these things results in a product that isn't created for the medium that it will eventually be presented in.

4 Conclusions

This project has allowed Copper Candle to shape the development of its live, virtual performance platform, *Copper House*. Understanding the role of the audience is essential to predicting the type of market that might want to purchase tickets and feel part of a community of live virtual theatre audiences.

As was established early in this chapter, it is still unknown what the market is for this industry as different models emerge, and artists attempt to create work that remediates their existing methods and creative styles. The findings of this research project have demonstrated that liveness isn't *necessary*, but it is *useful*. Knowing that there are times when you can prioritise quality is helpful to artists who know that because a section is repeatable and passive that it could be pre-recorded and mixed with live content which would help reduce production costs.

Having said that, the flexibility to perform live supports the iterative nature of theatre design and production development, allowing artists to continue to refine and develop a piece of work right up until it eventually needs to be performed.

Because audiences enjoyed the live interaction with the performer, it justifies the need for live performance. Seeing as the medium being used is a game application, even if it is running on a PC or a web browser, it could be argued that live interaction is necessary for the medium to be viable. If this is the case, it supports the idea that *all* virtual theatre should use live performance because a static, passive experience isn't what audiences want from a game application.

The most important conclusion drawn from this project is that the assumption that audiences value shared experiences was proven to be true. The interaction with the other audience members and the resulting feeling of connectedness was considered highest as a benefit for viewing live entertainment in this format. The feeling of liveness was more to do with this than the performers themselves by using scheduled and shared experiences to encourage a feeling of togetherness for audiences.

Acknowledgements The Copper Candle team, sub-contractors, and guest performers.

Andrew Voller, Rory Foster, Enrique Munoz Jimenez, Nikki Watson, Marissa Martin, Sophia Woodley, Victoria Simpson and James Simpson.

Integration of Smart Glasses for Knowledge Transfer in Industrial Remote Maintenance: Learnings from Practice

Anuja Hariharan, Monika Risling, Artur Felic, and Tobias Ostertag

1 Company Description

CAS Software AG was founded in 1986 and is led and managed by Martin Hubschneider. More than 400 co-creators work together on the CAS Campus in Karlsruhe, Germany, on leading software solutions of the industry that are used across several industries. The company's product portfolio includes cloud-based customer relationship management (CRM) systems and product and quote configurators that help organisations build successful and sustainable business relationships, make better use of corporate knowledge, and increase the efficiency of their employees. The products of the company are customised to several industries, including automobile, energy and utilities industry, research and education institutions, aviation industry, mechanical and plant engineering,

A. Hariharan (✉) • M. Risling • A. Felic • T. Ostertag
Future Labs, CAS Software AG, Karlsruhe, Germany
e-mail: a.hariharan@g-i-m.com; artur.felic@cas.de; tobias.ostertag@cas.de

T. Jung, M. C. tom Dieck (eds.), *XR-Metaverse Cases*, Business Guides on the Go,
https://doi.org/10.1007/978-3-031-30566-5_7

and manufacturing companies. Over 400,000 users worldwide work with CAS Software products every day.

2 Project Summary

Knowledge transfer is defined as "the conveyance of knowledge from one place, person, system or ownership to another" (Liyanage et al., 2009). Service and maintenance processes in particular require efficient knowledge transfer methods, where knowledge is rarely documented and important skills are limited to a few people (Webel et al., 2013; Zhou et al., 2008). The current worldwide pandemic has necessitated remote digital service processes and collaborative digital tools. These tools should enable information and knowledge exchange between employees of different levels of expertise (Wang et al., 2014) as well as achieve remote services seamlessly with available personnel on the customer end, where conducting service procedures with own maintenance personnel is time-consuming and expensive.

Augmented reality (AR) smart glasses have been identified as a powerful supporting technology in various tasks such as product design, assembly, maintenance, quality control, and material handling (Syberfeldt et al., 2017). In the area of maintenance, the crucial advantages of smart glasses lie in moving away from hand-held devices to head-mounted devices and an alternative control system by voice (Quint et al., 2017; Schulzrinne, 2018). Del Amo et al. (2018) present a systematic review to identify the relations between AR visualisation techniques in authoring, context awareness, and interaction analysis in the context of maintenance applications, to identify which knowledge transfer goals can be achieved by AR. According to Fu et al. (2010), remote maintenance allows time-saving to the traditional process of 60–90%. Despite these exceeding advantages reported in research, adoption of AR in practice by manufacturing companies has been slow (Syberfeldt et al., 2017).

In this project, we investigate the usability and acceptance aspects of augmented reality glasses for maintenance processes of a German manufacturing SME. A voice-controlled augmented reality application was designed, developed, and evaluated. Evaluation results of employees of the manufacturing SME with real-time maintenance use cases are presented. The chapter concludes with an outlook and implications for SMEs in adopting smart glass technology for maintenance in practice.

3 Project Details

The design science research methodology (Peffers et al., 2007) was adopted to define the requirements, design and develop a solution artefact, and evaluate and disseminate information about the artefact. Specifically, requirements were gathered by analysing the current maintenance process of the SME and proposing customer journeys for the targeted maintenance process. Touchpoints with existing CRM systems were identified, and actions and interactions of the service expert and the customer with the intended remote application were prioritised. These requirements were verified by means of in-depth interviews with service experts, and preliminary evaluations of mockup designs.

A comparison of state-of-the-art smart glasses for remote maintenance revealed several advantages of the Realwear[1] head-mounted tablets (HMT) for remote collaboration. (1) The availability of an open-source API compatible for building Unity and Android applications and (2) the availability of documentation and an online support community were two important factors in favour thereof. Moreover, (3) the RealWear enables adaption to the voice control system with its embedded API for WearML, the mark-up language of RealWear. The remote service application was built on Android, and components such as video calling and communication with CRM system were integrated over the Android base. A dedicated open-source video call server was hosted, thus enabling manufacturers to have a data-compliant way to communicate and store their sensitive data.

The remote service application generated identification numbers for each service request, which were sent to both the service personnel and the customer (as confirmation and e-mail invitation). Video call invitations were automatically generated for the specific machine type and

[1] https://realwear.com/products/hmt-1/

service problem and sent along with the e-mail invitation to the assigned personnel. On the application, the list of previous service sessions was fetched from the cloud-enabled CRM system SmartWe2,[2] from a dedicated tenant (database silo) using its REST API. Video calls were initiated by the service employee on the smart glasses using voice command, allowing multiple personnel to join at the same time, from different networks. Video sessions were recorded and cloud links were integrated on the CRM[3] tenant. The CRM tenant thus stored and visualised the complete overview of the progress of the maintenance sessions and tickets, as well as information on video recordings, service-call history, images taken during the service processes, and the corresponding contact details of the service personnel and customer. The information can be administered with the required rights and permissions, to ensure that only relevant service personnel have access to the service process.

4 Evaluation

The evaluation was carried out in three phases, wherein the results of each phase were incorporated iteratively into the next phase. The first evaluation was a usability and feature comparison test to evaluate the feature layout, particularly due to the constraints of the screen in the form of design mockups. The second evaluation aimed to evaluate the first prototype with smart glasses. Here, employees of a German SME software provider performed a mock maintenance task by assembling wooden blocks with instructions from another colleague remotely. They provided feedback on usability and specific features of the app, in addition to open feedback. The third evaluation was conducted with the employees of the manufacturer. Participants had to perform a typically occurring maintenance task remotely, with help of an experienced service team at a German SME manufacturer. Aspects such as high noise levels, intermittent network, and environmental lighting issues were also present in this evaluation, thus mimicking conditions of real-life usage.

[2] https://smartwe.de/en/

[3] https://realwear.com/blog/designing-realwear-hands-free-wearhf/

Feedback on AR suitability, usability, and feature design was gathered from 20 participants in each evaluation. Think-aloud protocols (Kussmaul & Tirkkonen-Condit, 1995; Jääskeläinen, 2010) were used during evaluations, where feedback from the users were directly recorded in a structured protocol. The System Usability Scale (SUS) was used to obtain a "global view of subjective assessments of usability" (Brooke, 1996). The SUS is based on a Likert scale (Brooke, 1996; Baumgartner et al., 2021) and has also been used in the analysis of wearable devices (Liang et al., 2018). Acceptance of smart glasses in the area of the usual tasks of an employee was investigated with the questionnaire of Berkemeier et al. (2017). Finally, the AR suitability questionnaire was adapted from Palmarini et al. (2017) to gauge suitability of smart glasses for the given maintenance task, as well as to assess whether AR content and annotations are considered a necessity by the users.

The results of all three evaluations showed that the majority of the participants were enthusiastic about the concept of the prototype. The fictitious as well as real-life maintenance task was fulfilled during the call with the service employee by all participants. In the third evaluation, participants reported that the application allows manufacturers to save their average maintenance time by 46% (measured in days), in comparison to their existing duration. The acceptance of the smart glass application (Realwear HMT-1) was dependent on the use case and requirement of the remote maintenance process. Usability scores of the application were, however, high for both non-maintenance and maintenance firm's employees. This resulted from the use of the recommended UX design guidelines by RealWear HMT3 and the improvements based on findings of previous evaluations. The reported acceptance scores in the second evaluation (by the software provider enterprise) were lower in comparison to those reported by the manufacturing enterprise employees in the third evaluation. Augmented reality content and annotations were not reported to be necessary for a successful application and adoption in this specific use case but was viewed upon as a helpful add-on. The prototype application was coded with open-source libraries and environments, and this information was communicated to the participants, before gathering feedback on privacy concerns. Open-source and dedicated servers are expected to allow SMEs to implement prototypes without lock-in problems, as well as achieve improved digital sovereignty and reduced privacy concerns surrounding the application. This was confirmed by the correlation between low reported privacy concerns and high acceptance scores in the two evaluations, as reported by the participants from the software provider as well as the manufacturing enterprise.

5 Future Outlook and Conclusion

This work demonstrated the process of developing a remote smart glass-based maintenance process for an SME. Whilst usability of the remote service application was reported to be high, the acceptance of technology was dependent on the need for remote processes and digital tools. Acceptance was improved further by integrating the remote tools with existing CRM and maintenance management systems, thus creating a seamless process for the service technician as well as the remote customer.

Limitations in the current design and evaluation process mainly involved the external circumstances of the global COVID-19 pandemic, which led to assumptions during the development and evaluation phase, such as social distancing measures, as well as in the evaluation process—where a complete remote evaluation at the manufacturer was designed. These measures might have led to crucial information about the maintenance process being overlooked during the evaluation. Further, the application was tested on one specific device, the RealWear HMT-1, which might have led to device-specific advantages as well as disadvantages influencing the acceptance scores. Another general limitation in the use of a remote maintenance application is the availability of a stable network connection and adapting video calls for low bandwidth requirements. As of today, there is a lack of ubiquitous high-speed Internet connection, particularly in Germany (Rauschnabel et al., 2015). This resulted in difficult circumstances for the video calls which partly reflected in the usability ratings.

As future work, the above-mentioned points need to be revisited and improved upon in further evaluations with pilot customers. Second, a detailed business analysis should be conducted and a revenue model for different companies would be necessary to facilitate further development and adoption of the technology. Moreover, the application should be developed for different smart glasses towards an accessible and generic remote maintenance application. Since most state-of-the-art smart glasses are Android-based devices, developing an Android application is a promising step in this direction. Integration with existing CRM systems should be expanded to allow for more possibilities—such as re-ordering of service machinery, or pre-shipping maintenance parts before scheduling the remote service procedure. Finally, long-term safety and health consequences on employees for wearing the RealWear HMT-1 have to be investigated, for successful adoption by employees and customers (Kim et al., 2016).

This research provides learnings from practice to increase adoption of smart glasses, particularly in manufacturing industries, where remote maintenance has become the need of the hour. Future work in providing a seamless experience across existing (CRM) systems would not only improve the acceptance of the smart glasses in maintenance but also extend it to areas of application in manufacturing—such as design, development, quality control, and other scenarios necessitating remote collaboration.

References

Baumgartner, J., Ruettgers, N., Hasler, A., Sonderegger, A., & Sauer, J. (2021). Questionnaire experience and the hybrid System Usability Scale: Using a novel concept to evaluate a new instrument. *International Journal of Human-Computer Studies, 147*, 102575.

Berkemeier, L., Werning, S., Zobel, B., Ickerott, I., & Thomas, O. (2017). Der Kunde als Dienstleister: Akzeptanz und Gebrauchstauglichkeit von Smart Glasses im Self-Service. *HMD, 54*(5), 781–794.

Brooke, J. (1996). In P. W. Jordan, B. Thomas, I. L. McClelland, & B. Weerdmeester (Eds.), *SUS. A quick and dirty usability scale: Usability evaluation in industry* (pp. 189–194). Taylor and Francis.

del Amo, I. F., Erkoyuncu, J. A., Roy, R., Palmarini, R., & Onoufriou, D. (2018). A systematic review of Augmented Reality content-related techniques for knowledge transfer in maintenance applications. *Computers in Industry, 103*, 47–71.

Fu, H., Pao, H. T., & Tseng, C. L. (2010). Internet based remote customer services. In *2010 IEEE Region 8 International Conference on Computational Technologies in Electrical and Electronics Engineering. SIBIRCON 2010* (pp. 733–735); Irkutsk, Russia, 11–15 July 2010; [proceedings]. Piscataway, NJ: IEEE.

Jääskeläinen, R. (2010). Think-aloud protocol. In Y. Gambier & L. van Doorslaer (Eds.), *Handbook of translation studies* (Vol. 1, pp. 371–373). John Benjamins.

Kim, S., Nussbaum, M. A., & Gabbard, J. L. (2016). Augmented Reality "Smart Glasses" in the workplace: Industry perspectives and challenges for worker safety and health. *IIE Transactions on Occupational Ergonomics and Human Factors, 4*(4), 253–258.

Kussmaul, P., & Tirkkonen-Condit, S. (1995). Think-aloud protocol analysis in translation studies. *TTR, 8*(1), 177–199. https://doi.org/10.7202/037201ar

Liang, J., Xian, D., Liu, X., Fu, J., Zhang, X., Tang, B., & Lei, J. (2018). Usability study of mainstream wearable fitness devices: Feature analysis and system usability scale evaluation. *JMIR mHealth and uHealth, 6*(11), e11066. https://doi.org/10.2196/11066

Liyanage, C., Elhag, T., Ballal, T., & Li, Q. (2009). Knowledge communication and translation–a knowledge transfer model. *Journal of Knowledge Management.*

Palmarini, R., Erkoyuncu, J. A., & Roy, R. (2017). An innovative process to select Augmented Reality (AR) technology for maintenance. *Procedia CIRP, 59*, 23–28.

Peffers, K., Tuunanen, T., Rothenberger, M. A., & Chatterjee, S. (2007). A design science research methodology for information systems research. *Journal of Management Information Systems, 24*(3), 45–77.

Quint, F., Loch, F., & Bertram, P. (2017). The challenge of introducing AR in industry – Results of a participative process involving maintenance engineers. *Procedia Manufacturing, 11*, 1319–1323. https://doi.org/10.1016/j.promfg.2017.07.260

Rauschnabel, P., Brem, A., & Ro, Y. (2015). Augmented Reality smart glasses. Definition, conceptual insights, and managerial importance.

Schulzrinne, H. (2018). *Proceedings of the 15th EAI International Conference on Mobile and Ubiquitous Systems Computing, Networking and Services*. ACM (ACM Other conferences).

Syberfeldt, A., Danielsson, O., & Gustavsson, P. (2017). *Augmented Reality smart glasses in the smart factory: Product evaluation guidelines and review of available products* (pp. 9118–9130). https://doi.org/10.1109/ACCESS.2017.2703952

Wang, J., Feng, Y., Zeng, C., & Li, S. (2014). An augmented reality based system for remote collaborative maintenance instruction of complex products. In IEEE (Ed.), *2014 IEEE International Conference on Automation Science and Engineering (CASE). Taipei, 18–22 August 2014* (pp. 309–314).

Webel, S., Bockholt, U., Engelke, T., Gavish, N., Olbrich, M., & Preusche, C. (2013). An augmented reality training platform for assembly and maintenance skills. *Robotics and Autonomous Systems, 61*(4), 398–403. https://doi.org/10.1016/j.robot.2012.09.013

Zhou, F., Duh, H. B.-L., & Billinghurst, M. (2008). Trends in augmented reality tracking, interaction and display: A review of ten years of ISMAR. In IEEE Computer Society (Ed.), *2008 7th IEEE/ACM International Symposium on Mixed and Augmented Reality* (pp. 193–202). ISMAR, Cambridge, UK, 15–18 September 2008.

Safety Is Everything: Design of an AR·VR Training Simulator for Radiation Emergency Response

DongSeok Song

1 Company Description

Novatech is at the forefront of the Extended Reality (XR) market. Novatech addresses current workplace safety issues, particularly in the industrial sector, and aims to provide reliable solutions to ensure worker safety through its XR technology. Novatech's services provide realistic simulations that can be used in employee training to reduce risks in bio-hazard environments.

Founded in 2015, Novatech has worked with both large and small industrial safety-related clients since its inception, and is valued by most for maximising their return on investment.

Novatech's primary objective is to provide products and services that improve safety and increase productivity in the industrial workplace. Novatech's XR technology provides a realistic simulation that reduces the

D. Song (✉)
Novatech, Seoul, Korea
e-mail: song@novatek.kr

T. Jung, M. C. tom Dieck (eds.), *XR-Metaverse Cases*, Business Guides on the Go,
https://doi.org/10.1007/978-3-031-30566-5_8

operational burden on companies, minimises the costs incurred and saves time. The virtual environment can be used as a training system to help professionals become more familiar with emergency response at biohazard sites such as nuclear plants. The service also secures efficient product exportation for companies, which improves customer satisfaction and leverages their competitiveness. Novatech also brings innovative, therapeutic value to the medical market with its XR-based rehabilitation gears.

2 Project Summary

The "Design of an AR·VR Training Simulator for Radiation Emergency Response" project aims to create a realistic and immersive training simulator for emergency responders in the event of a radiation emergency. The project will use both augmented reality (AR) and virtual reality (VR) technologies to simulate the potential dangers of a radiation emergency and provide training for emergency responders to learn how to respond effectively. The training simulator will feature a 3D virtual environment that will allow emergency responders to explore and interact with the simulated environment. The simulator will provide a realistic representation of radiation sources, as well as simulated radiation detection equipment and protective gear. The use of AR technology will allow for the overlay of digital information onto the real world, allowing for more immersive and interactive training scenarios. The project will be developed in collaboration with emergency responders and radiation safety experts to ensure the accuracy and relevance of the training scenarios. The ultimate goal of the project is to provide emergency responders with a safe and effective way to train for radiation emergency response, which will ultimately help to protect the public and the environment in the event of a real-world emergency. The completed training simulator will be an innovative and effective tool for training emergency responders, and has the potential to significantly improve the effectiveness of emergency response efforts in the event of a radiation emergency.

3 Project Details

3.1 Challenge

In order for the government to guarantee they are delivering health and safety policy infrastructure for employee, the company must ensure the workforce are fully trained and competent in the work they are undertaking. Most training and experience occur in emergency environments where there is a necessity for a prompt decision. Nuclear accidents can be irreversible and catastrophic, so it is important to prevent accidents and respond quickly in the event of an emergency. There are currently 24 nuclear power plants in operation in Korea (Fig.1) with four more under construction in Uljin and Ulsan, Gyeongbuk.

The purpose of the Practice of VR Radiation Exposure Treatment Training is to improve your ability to respond to radiation emergencies by practising medical techniques and behaviours that can only be used in an emergency, or training by implementing the environment and equipment you will need to treat radiation compound injury with virtual reality.

Fig. 1 Example of a nuclear power plant: Kori Nuclear in Korea

3.2 Solution

This solution was developed as an alternative to standard education and training systems for radiation emergency situations, as it restricts the practical description of radiation disasters and emergencies in real situations.

The system is also used to give the medical team a better understanding of site environments and risks even if they've never experienced the situation where there is radiation exposure before—closing a gap between the real world and the virtual world in a workflow (Fig. 2).

The practice of the treatment process has various contents such as granting a specified virtual space, starting training with the virtual patient influx, and assigning simulated patient situations. This treatment process is including how to configure the equipment for each level of radioactive contamination, severity of damage, symptoms of exposure, etc.

Also, the training team can implement treatment measures for decontamination. For example, they can learn how to classify patients with combined radiation damage efficiently and get knowledge about dry and wet decontamination and medical technique. Furthermore, the whole process of medical treatment is included in this training simulator. It is also important to know not only the way to treat radiation exposure patients but also the process for transferring patients to another hospital, hospitalisation, outpatient tracking, and finally returning home safely.

We are developing the 3-Point Tracking Technology to see the actions of other treatments that calculates the position of the head-mounted display and the position information of the hand to generate the movement of the entire body to visualise the movement of the other person.

Applying URP standards for Universal Render Pipeline technology is also implemented to provide realistic visuals by implementing materialisation of realistic visuals and application of global illumination, lighting, and shadow effects.

The main treatment process is VR triage that is providing a virtual environment with an on-site radiation emergency clinic (tent) and portal monitor. At the beginning of the training, trainees start to classify the injured patients with combined radiation damage by various levels of contamination, severity, and appearance in the Portal Monitor to separate contaminated/non-contaminated patients. The severity is divided

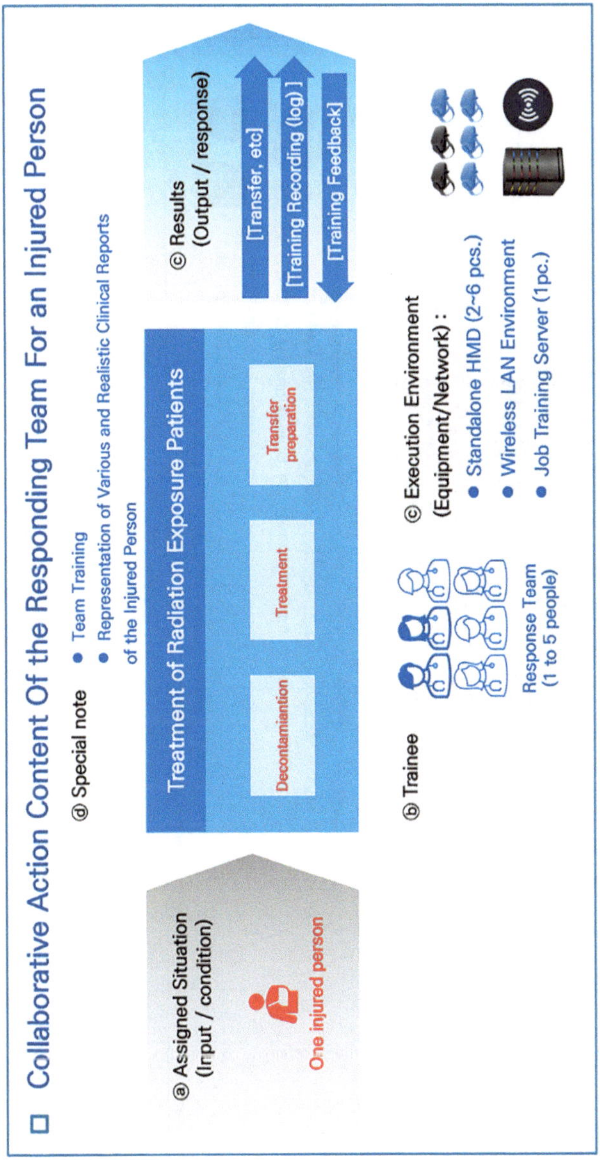

Fig. 2 The practice of the treatment process for radiation exposure patients

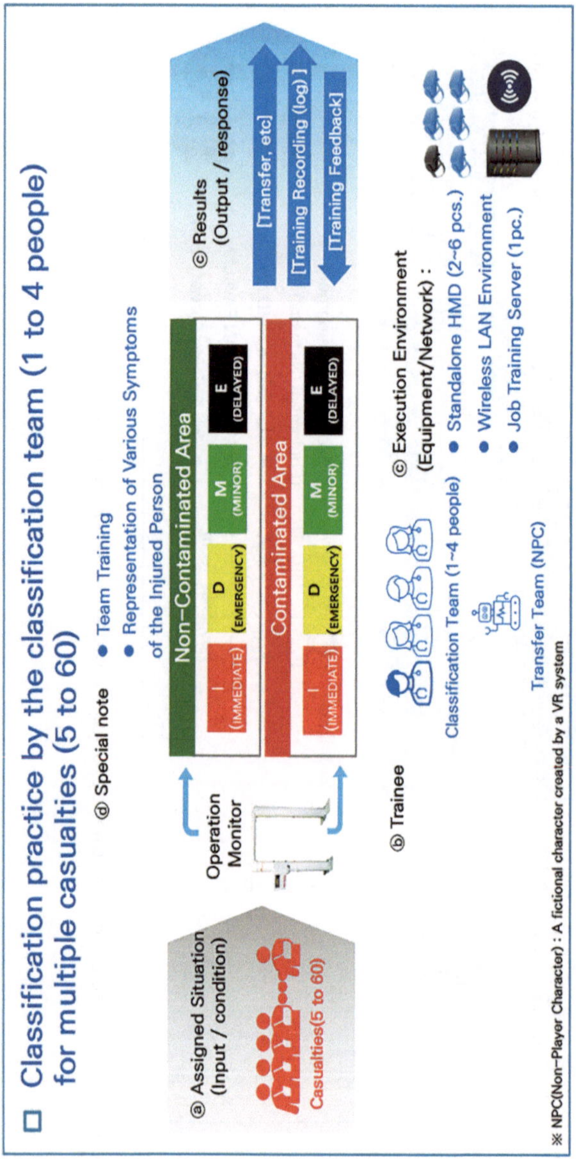

Fig. 3 VR Triage

into four stages: immediate, delayed, minimal, and expectant. Performance assessment is provided in every training simulation after completing a triage and the trainer can get prompt feedback on the training (Fig. 3).

Real-time synchronisation of actions with AI NPCs (Artificial Intelligence Non-Player Characters) was implemented. Patient NPCs implemented with artificial intelligence behave according to assigned attribute values. This enables orientation to the actual situation and allows the trainer to focus on training. The simulator has the function of creating a representative character with a 3D scan and implementing 60 patient characters by making a difference.

3.3 Benefits

There is specific effectiveness for simulating the radiation response training (Fig. 4). First, the benefit is trainee is getting proficiency in complex classification based on severity classification and radiological characteristics, and each member of the Joint Radiation Emergency Care Centre has comprehension of the roles and tasks given by the simulator.

Second, the trainee can expect proficiency in implementing RFID, NFC, and AR glass according to unexplainable radioactive contamination situations. Third, understanding of key processes and detailed

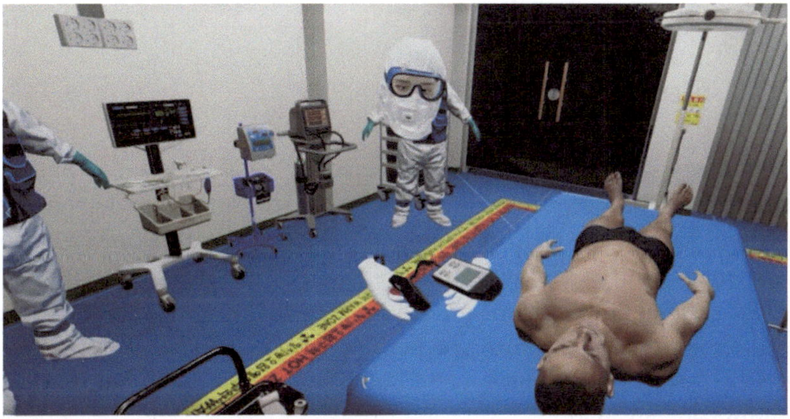

Fig. 4 Virtual reality training in use by Novatech radiation response simulator

procedures are improving in field clinics. Four, they can expect the familiarisation of emergency medical personnel with how to use measuring equipment and improvement of field operation proficiency by equipment.

The eventual purpose is to strengthen emergency medical personnel's capacity to respond to hospitals and identify the factors that need to be considered through the process of solving it in the process of responding to several casualties accompanied by radioactive contamination entering the hospital (Fig. 5).

4 Feedback from End Users

Following successful nationwide safety training, there is excitement within the Novatech Radiation Response Training Simulator as the business is leveraging modern-day technology to an even greater extent. Users of the simulator have remarked upon the realisation that the training system has highlighted their "response in an emergency situation". For most medical staff, it is not that simple to experience high-risk environments such as a radioactive leak.

Learning the process to treat patients is properly presented for each content, and it is evaluated as the contents are appropriately organised in consideration of visibility and readability; the best thing is the representation realistically to feel a sense of reality in the virtual situation.

5 Outlook/Roadmap

Technology planning will be completed by establishing the purpose, development concept map, content, and technical implementation methodology for the eight content components to be developed as virtual augmented reality training simulators.

The general development procedure is carried out by adding detailed requirements through prototype development and reflection of training participants' needs to the general development procedure to maximise training effectiveness.

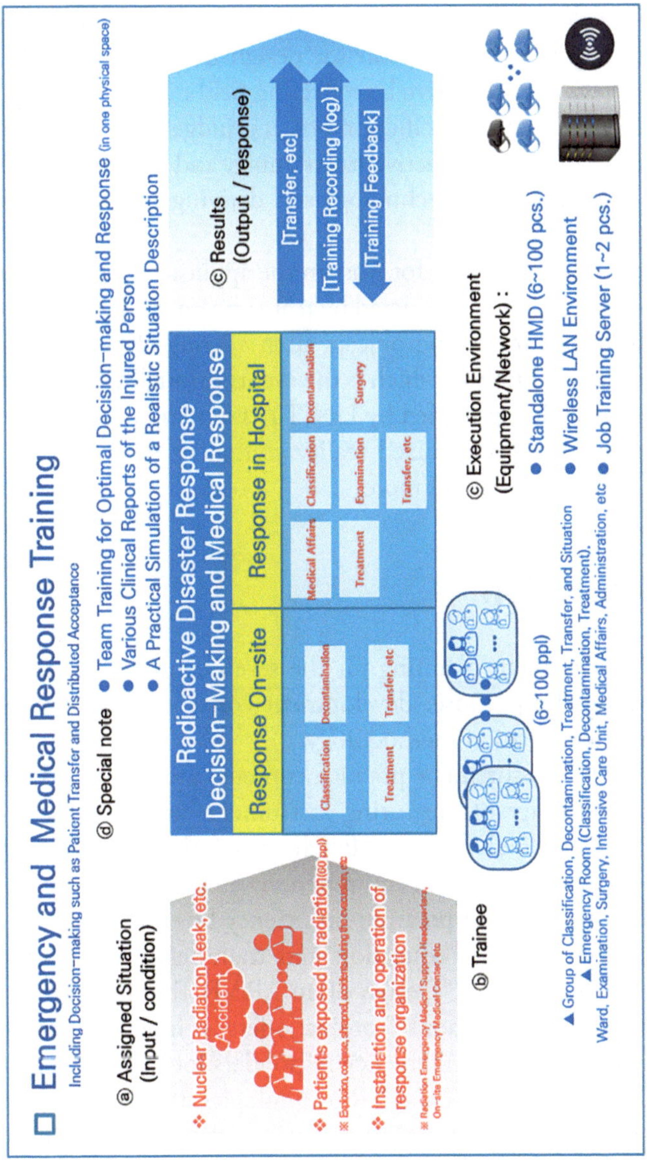

Fig. 5 VR radiological disaster hospital response decision training system

The complete development process starts with planning; then design and prototype development is the next for the following steps. The development team give a confirmation for design in order to check if it is complete or is to be alternative by reflecting field needs.

In the development of specific content, it is judged that the application of mixed reality (MR) is effective for training, and accordingly, research on analysing mixed reality technology and deriving application methods is conducted.

Novatech uses Hololens 2 for glass in the application, and the analysis target for technologies is conducted by real-time image mapping technology of objects and modelling objects after wearing glass and asynchronous processing technology which is the events through UniRX (Reactive Extensions for Unity) provided by UNITY, a development engine. Also, the method of producing mixed reality content is used by Hololens 2 including difficulty level and more.

6 Conclusion

Technical development planning for the seven contents was completed by establishing the purpose, development concept map, content, and technical implementation methodology.

AR and MR measurement practice contents are developed, and the appearance and usage of measuring instruments are virtualised; hence, users can learn freely at any time. Furthermore, the simulator enhances learning how to use measuring equipment by emergency medical personnel and improves on-site operation proficiency by equipment and maximises the effectiveness of education and training through convenient search. In conclusion, the "Design of an AR·VR Training Simulator for Radiation Emergency Response" project offers an innovative solution to the challenges of training emergency responders for radiation emergency response. By using both AR and VR technologies, the simulator provides a realistic and immersive training experience that allows responders to gain practical experience in a simulated environment without risking their safety or the safety of the public.

An Audience with a Hero: A Conversational VR Experience

Sarah Coward, David Jackson, and Marsha Courneya

1 Company Description

In The Room Global Ltd is a media-tech company specialising in conversational media technologies. The company's software integrates voice recognition, AI, and exclusive audio-visual content to recreate the experience of a unique face-to-face encounter: enabling audiences to ask questions to a notable person, on demand, 24/7.

The company's work evolved from The Forever Project, an educational initiative at the National Holocaust Centre and Museum. The Forever Project was designed to preserve the experience of "meeting" a Holocaust survivor in order to preserve this experience for young people who might never have the opportunity to meet one of these witnesses in person.

S. Coward (✉)
In The Room Global Ltd, London, UK
e-mail: sarah.coward@intheroom.global; sarah.coward@foreverproject.co.uk

D. Jackson • M. Courneya
School of Digital Arts, Manchester Metropolitan University, Manchester, UK
e-mail: d.j.jackson@mmu.ac.uk; m.courneya@mmu.ac.uk

T. Jung, M. C. tom Dieck (eds.), *XR-Metaverse Cases*, Business Guides on the Go,
https://doi.org/10.1007/978-3-031-30566-5_9

Through a life-size interactive video projection, users could ask questions to the image of the survivor using their voice, and receive an answer immediately: providing a new way to engage with the testimonies of multiple Holocaust survivors (Coward et al., 2017).

The company now works across platforms and industries, with its technology being used to create experiences delivered via web browsers for mobile access, life-size in-venue experiences, or immersive experiences in VR.

2 Project Summary

The Audience with a Hero project was a collaboration between In The Room Global Ltd., Bright White Ltd. (an award-winning design company which had worked on the original Forever Project), and Manchester Metropolitan University (with involvement from senior staff from the School of Digital Arts). Beginning in 2019, this 18-month project sought to develop the principles of In The Room's work and apply these to a VR environment to create a unique and immersive encounter. The project was funded within the Audience of the Future programme by UK Research and Innovation through the Industrial Strategy Challenge Fund and Innovate UK.

Audience with a Hero centred on a single "hero" as its subject: musician and producer, Nile Rodgers. Its focus was on creating a powerful, engaging encounter with a hero in virtual space by developing and testing new and/or improved production processes which created a sense of "presence".

With the concept of "presence" in mind, the production approach was designed specifically for use in an out-of-home virtual reality experience to heighten immersion.

3 Project Details

During the 18-month project, a transdisciplinary approach was required to create an effective, engaging experience, the principles of which could be replicated efficiently. In building a virtual reality experience based on a person's real identity, the design challenges led the production team to investigate how human conversational dynamics could best be virtually represented. A direct objective for the project was also maximising the ability to facilitate the feeling of "presence" (central to the project vision's notion of an encounter), which can be summed up as "the pre-reflexive sensation of 'being' in an environment, real or virtual, which results from the capacity to carry out intuitively one's intentions within that environment" (Riva et al., 2014) [or more simply, "the perceptual illusion of non-mediation" (Lombard & Ditton, 1997)]. Specifically, the intention was to develop within the user a sense that the hero was present in the same space as the user him/herself.

In order to provide a more compelling and naturalistic interaction with Nile, project team collaborators conducted design research into topics such as *proxemics*, *prosodics*, and *parasocial relationships*. Proxemics research considered the position of Nile in relation to a participant in this particular encounter and the type of high-quality audio-visual capture that would be technically reliable in a high-pressure studio environment whilst providing the desired effect. Prosodics investigation considered how best to interview the subject in a way that would mimic natural conversational dynamics. Lastly, parasocial relationships were considered as a consequence of having a celebrity as the subject of the Audience with a Hero project, which necessitated research into interpersonal dynamics with talent. This resulted in exploring how the study of parasocial relationship formation might intersect with the experience and affect the public's perception of Nile as a media figure. The study of parasocial relationships, which are the attachments formed between a member of the public and a media figure through one-way channels such as television (Horton & Richard Wohl, 1956), continues to gain sociological relevance through the deepening complexity of mediated relationships between celebrities and the public (Kim & Song, 2016; Yuksel & Labrecque, 2016).

The design and production process was highly creative with significant complexity, including advanced video production, natural language data and asset design, creative scripting, and technical development.

The VR project was experienced by audience members as follows: after putting on the VR headset, the user can see an empty chair in front of them. Out of sight, and to the side, they can hear guitar music playing. The musician and guitarist Nile Rodgers then emerges from offset, walking towards the chair and sitting down in front of the user. He introduces himself and initiates an opportunity for the user to ask him a question. There then follows an engagement in a conversational exchange allowing the user to ask questions using their voice. After each question is posed by the user, they see and hear Nile Rodgers answering in front of them.

To produce the experience Nile Rodgers was interviewed before a stereoscopic camera rig over 2 days to capture real answers to over 350 questions about his life and career. These media clips were indexed as part of a conversational agent system that allowed participants to ask these questions using their voice and see and hear Nile Rodgers responding from the pre-recorded assets.

Matching what was said by the participant to the appropriate clip of Nile Rodgers was managed through conversational agent technology and natural language processing (NLP). For more human-like interactions between Nile and audiences, conversational agent (CA) and design research sought to find better methods for rapid agent development that were more accurate and reliable in response to audience questions.

In addition to the creation of the VR experience itself, the project sought to find production methods and efficiencies that would not only minimise the cost of development in these experiences but also make VR experiences more compelling. In order to evaluate the effectiveness of production innovations, it was necessary to evaluate the quality of the experience for users in terms of a powerful, engaging encounter with a hero in virtual space. Evaluation questions were devised to ascertain how participants felt about their virtual meeting and about Nile himself "as a person" after the experience, in order to provide insight into the value of authenticity in a virtual encounter. Questions in the user evaluation also addressed NLP and presence by, amongst other questions, asking participants whether they were able to "follow their own line of questioning" during the experience.

COVID-19 restrictions resulted in a small number of people being able to test and evaluate the full VR version of the experience. The majority of the testing needed to be conducted on a large flatscreen using a fixed perspective video input where the image of Nile Rodgers was comparatively small in relation to the screen size. This difference provided useful qualitative evidence of the particular affordances of VR.

4 Feedback from End Users

Almost all (97%: 28 of 29 participants) reported a sense of having met with Nile and having had a conversation. This was consistent across flatscreen and VR tests. Factors that enabled this sense of a meeting were the facility to ask a variety of interesting, curated questions and for Nile to answer them accurately and engagingly, a sense that Nile was engaged with the Q&A process of answering the questions put to him, and the novelty of being greeted and said goodbye to in a convincing and personally touching way. Factors that detracted from the "magic" were repeated answers, fallback intents (e.g. Nile saying: "I didn't record an answer to that question"), or technical problems.

However, whereas flatscreen participants commented on the framing, testing environment, and quality of the image, comments on these aspects were absent in the feedback from VR testers where a more immersive experience was achieved. All participants reported the sense of a palpable physical proximity to Nile when wearing a VR headset. Due to the contingent nature of the flatscreen test it was expected that it would only be sufficient to properly test aspects of the user journey and interactivity in the experience. However, whilst taking into account the relatively small sample size, it was clear that all of the research done on proxemics, 3D filming, and post-production had created a best in-class VR experience that made it feel as though the participant was sat in the room with Nile. This was evidenced in all interviews and observations of the tests. At one point, one participant laughed and cried out "Ah! Don't sit on my knee!

I've only just met you!". Whilst this was an extreme reaction it highlighted the sense of Nile's presence in the experience:

> "I think the room, the way that the atmospherics of the room were shot, it felt more like a one-on-one. It felt like it was just him and me. There was nobody else."
>
> VR Participant 1
>
> "It was more real than I expected. The fact that you could look down and see his shoes. When he stood up, I leaned back! It felt like he was present."
>
> VR Participant 3

In support of this observation in the feedback was the frequency with which some of the flatscreen participants expressed a wish to have experienced the work in VR:

> That isolation of being in a headset [would] draw you in a bit.
>
> If you had VR headsets though, if you felt he was physically there, that would be even better. Because he was only small on this screen, but if you were immersed in it, that would be brilliant.

In addition to testing the experience itself, a small follow-up study allowed the team to informally investigate the opportunity for further research in the area of synthetic representations of real people. This early testing confirmed the importance of authenticity in the representation of media figures. Participant feedback suggested that an audience member's perception of these figures, and their emotional reaction to them, is affected by whether they believe footage to be real or not. Knowing that the footage *was* authentic, and therefore seen to represent the person accurately, was important. Conversely, issues of trust and ethics arose if the footage was considered to be synthetic. These issues are important considerations for further research.

5 Future Outlook

The VR development and subsequent challenges related to COVID-19 acted as a springboard for the planned web launch of the experience. The learnings from testing informed the design approach to the browser-based version of the Nile Rodgers experience, "In The Room with Nile Rodgers", which was successfully launched in March 2021. It has also informed In The Room's consideration of its scalable conversational media platform for the production of web-based experiences in commercial and cultural settings. Meanwhile, the team has developed a core efficacy and efficiency in terms of developing high-quality VR that makes the production of meaningful and convincing experiences feasible for the representation of real individuals within immersive environments. This has potential for informing other types of encounters within other immersive environments and displays, including augmented reality, holographic display, gaming, and metaverse environments.

The development of applications using synthetic media requires careful consideration given issues such as trust and authenticity, but might also present opportunity for further creative endeavour.

6 Conclusions

The alpha project testing provided significant and corroborated evidence that the Audience with a Hero project created a valuable, entertaining, and memorable experience. It reportedly left audience members with a sense of having met with a hero of popular music culture, often with a desire to return to "meet" with Nile and ask more questions. Whilst it would have been ideal to test with all users in VR, the project's flatscreen version allowed the team to evaluate key aspects of the project, in particular the interaction design and the central premise of the experience, i.e. creating a meaningful and engaging encounter with a "hero". The reactions of the test users demonstrated the significant potential in this area for future application across a range of industries and settings.

Finally, whilst the increasingly sophisticated affordances of synthetic media representation remain a further area of research, it is important to note that the project showed that the strength of the experience lies not only in its technical execution and design, but also the strength of Rodgers' career and personality as authentically portrayed, and the consequent connection with his fanbase eager to hear what he has to say (and play). This is an important consideration in the creative development and application of In The Room's approach, combining technical benefits with a method that is leveraging the power of human "presence".

Acknowledgements The consortium would like to thank UKRI/Innovate UK, Universal Music Group, Nile Rodgers and his management team, The National Portrait Gallery, and all key stakeholders who have contributed to making the Audience with a Hero project a success.

References

Coward, S., Ma, M., & Walker, C. (2017). *Question-answering virtual humans based on pre-recorded testimonies for Holocaust Education*.

Horton, D., & Richard Wohl, R. (1956). Mass communication and para-social interaction: Observations on intimacy at a distance. *Psychiatry, 19*(3), 215–230.

Kim, J., & Song, H. (2016). Celebrity's self-disclosure on Twitter and parasocial relationships: A mediating role of social presence. *Computers in Human Behavior, 62*, 570–577.

Lombard, M., & Ditton, T. (1997). At the heart of it all: The concept of presence. *Journal of Computer-Mediated Communication, 3*.

Riva, G., Waterworth, J., & Murray, D. (2014). *Interacting with presence: HCI and the sense of presence in computer mediated environment*. De Gruyter Open.

Yuksel, M., & Labrecque, L. I. (2016). 'digital Buddies': Parasocial interactions in social media. *Journal of Research in Interactive Marketing, 10*(4), 305–320.

Enhancing Continued Medical Education with Shared Immersive Spaces

Matthew Frese, Jesse Rowland, and Natalie Cregan-Evans

1 Company Description

1.1 Med Learning Group

Med Learning Group, a division of Ultimate Medical Academy, is a full-service accredited medical education company. It focuses on developing and implementing continuing education that improves the ability of healthcare professionals (HCPs) to provide optimal care to their patients. It designs programmes for physicians, nurses, pharmacists, and other HCPs and has a deep understanding of how to educate both specialised audiences and general practitioners.

M. Frese (✉)
Med Learning Group, Tampa, FL, USA
e-mail: mfrese@medlearninggroup.com

J. Rowland • N. Cregan-Evans
Igloo Vision, Craven Arms, UK
e-mail: jesse@igloovision.com; natalie@igloovision.com

T. Jung, M. C. tom Dieck (eds.), *XR-Metaverse Cases*, Business Guides on the Go,
https://doi.org/10.1007/978-3-031-30566-5_10

1.2 Igloo Vision

Based in the UK, with offices across America and Australasia, Igloo Vision develops software that powers shared immersive spaces. This software takes any digital content, including immersive VR or 360° content, and puts it into a space that anyone can get inside. The technology is used by clients across a wide range of industries including education, healthcare, utilities, real estate and more. By showing content in this way, groups can experience educational VR content at the same time, making it a shared learning experience.

2 Project Summary

Med Learning Group owns three Igloo immersive cylinders that it deploys at healthcare shows across the USA. The cylinders, which Med Learning Group calls its VR Rooms, immerse groups of HCPs in 3D content to educate them across a range of disciplines such as neurology, ophthalmology, psychiatry, immunology, and medical advancements in these. Med Learning Group applied a robust evaluation technique on two of its events in 2019 with results including:

- A 31% gain in knowledge—with 81% answering knowledge-based questions correctly after the activity compared to 62% beforehand.
- 98% of participants indicated the VR content enhanced the learning experience.
- 90% of participants indicated the VR content would improve recall of lessons learned.

3 Project Details

3.1 The Situation

Med Learning Group has expertise in developing both live and online activities for continued education programmes that are innovative, case-based, interactive, and patient-centric. Its team are experts in applying adult learning theory and principles to its programmes and, more importantly, understanding the nuances of its various audiences.

Its programmes cover topics and disciplines including:

- Oncology
- Neurology
- Psychiatry
- Infectious diseases
- Immunology
- Cardiovascular
- Respiratory
- Ophthalmology
- Transplants
- New medical advancements in these

The organisation is always looking for creative, innovative, and interactive ways to deliver results and value. It is vital that its education programmes resonate with the HCP audience, to deliver improved competence and improved patience outcomes.

Med Learning Group has been using virtual reality (VR) since 2013. Shortly after the launch of the first commercially available Oculus headset, Med Learning Group acquired 100 headsets and deployed them at a meeting. At the time of writing, it now owns over 600 headsets that it incorporates into its programmes.

Both medicine and technology are constantly evolving, along with the ways that people learn. As such, Med Learning Group wanted to remain innovative in its methods of education.

3.2 The Solution

Med Learning Group began investigating ways of sharing its immersive content with groups of people, so that they could experience the content all at the same time. In the course of its research, the company came across Igloo Vision's shared immersive spaces. Following a series of demos, Med Learning Group made an initial purchase of one Igloo cylinder. It now owns three Igloo immersive cylinders.

3.3 Details of the Igloo Immersive Spaces

Igloo Vision's immersive workspaces come in many shapes, sizes, and degrees of sophistication, from simple sales and presentation suites to powerful CAVE-type solutions. They are available to be retrofitted in existing rooms, as custom-built configurations, or stand-alone pop-up structures.

These workspaces integrate with any digital content and a wide range of everyday enterprise tools, including standard video conferencing platforms. They allow teams to work with several different types of content, in different formats, from different sources, all at the same time. Display technologies can be customised to suit a client's needs, whether LED screens or projectors.

Each Igloo immersive workspace is powered by an Igloo Immersive Media Player (IMP) and Igloo software.

Med Learning Group's cylinders are portable and deployed at various trade shows across North America. Each cylinder is equipped with 3D projectors. At shows, delegates are handed a pair of active-shutter 3D glasses, so that they can almost reach out and touch the content they're viewing. So that Med Learning Group could get the most out of the technology, Igloo provided training on the set-up, running, and derigging of the cylinders, enabling Med Learning Group to deploy them wherever it chooses.

The cylinders are branded with new covers for each trade show so that they make attractive showpieces for the delegates.

3.4 Why Med Learning Group Was Attracted to Igloo Immersive Technology

With its early investment in headsets, Med Learning Group had already seen great success with VR content and learned valuable lessons about how best it could be deployed. It wanted to find a way to extend the benefits:

- *Sharing the experience*—with Igloo's shared immersive spaces, whole groups could experience the VR content together and discuss it with each other in real time. Additionally, the 3D projection in the VR Rooms adds another level of immersion to the experience.
- *Leaving a lasting impression*—it's important that the care providers, clinicians, and other HCPs can apply their learnings to their work with patients. With the VR Rooms, the experience is more engaging than reading or watching a video and leads to higher levels of retention.
- *Expanding the content*—Med Learning Group had found that, when designing content for just VR headsets, it was best to keep it only a few minutes long because of the audience attention span. Inside its VR Rooms, it could make use of longer pieces of content. This also enabled it to incorporate the broader perspectives of the faculty that had advised on the content.
- *A portable solution*—Igloo's shared immersive spaces come in many shapes and sizes, including as custom-built configurations or stand-alone pop-up structures. Med Learning Group has been able to take its education programmes on the road across the USA with its travelling VR Rooms, sharing the experience with an even wider audience.

3.5 The VR Rooms in Action

The particular results discussed in this case study follow from Med Learning Group's use of its VR Rooms at two association events in 2019 as part of educational programmes on diabetes: ADA 2019 in San Francisco, California, and AADE in Houston, Texas.

The ADA VR Room hosted 801 participants, whilst the AADE VR Room hosted 601 participants.

At these events, Med Learning Group delivered education programmes on the impact and progression of diabetes to audiences made up of primary care providers, endocrinologists, nurse practitioners, physician assistants, pharmacists, and certified diabetes educators. Participants could take a pre- and post-event evaluation to measure the impact of the programme.

The VR Rooms were used to show a 4K 360° video of faculty introducing a diabetes case, sharing key data points, and introducing the VR experience to groups of between 5-to-15 people, all wearing 3D glasses. Participants could step right into the visualisations, almost reaching out to touch them.

3.6 Evaluating the Impact

Med Learning Group's educational programmes have seen considerable success, with its VR Rooms noted as adding to the learning experience. Highlights include:

- 93% of learners identified a commitment to a practice change based on the education.
- A 31% gain in knowledge—with 81% answering knowledge-based questions correctly after the activity compared to 62% beforehand.
- More than 9 out of 10 participants agreed that they would recommend the programme to their colleagues.
- 98% of participants indicated the VR content enhanced the learning experience.
- 90% of participants indicated the VR content would improve recall of lessons learned.

Table 1 End user feedback

Creating a memorable and unique experience	"It was a really dynamic experience, it really captured my attention, and everything was presented very clearly—it kept me engaged throughout." "It really brings everything to life, it's not just something you see on a page. You can get inside what you're learning about, and it makes things stick better in your mind when you can physically see the content."
Delivering education in an innovative way	"This was an excellent representation of diabetic retinopathy that was both complex but simplified so that clinicians could understand the impact of the disease." "This VR experience was a great way to learn about the differences between the types of insulin." "The experience puts you in the disease, and you feel like you're exploring it in a very understandable way—it's very impressive."
Taking learnings forward	"It'll be awesome to incorporate the learnings into clinical practice and share it with our patients." "I thought it was very visual and easy to learn, and I'm looking forward to bringing that to my patient care."

4 Feedback from End Users

Med Learning Group captured feedback and testimonials from attendees at the two shows across three main areas (Table 1):

5 Future Outlook/Roadmap

Going forward, Med Learning Group is building out another programme of events throughout 2022 to deploy its cylinders at.

At the height of the pandemic, the organisation pivoted to online-only events, for which it recreated a virtual exhibition area including a virtual Igloo to give online attendees an experience as close to the in-person one as possible. In the future, these online events will run alongside the in-person events, expanding its audience even further.

6 Conclusion

Med Learning Group's educational programmes have achieved excellent outcomes for HCPS, which will be passed on to those HCPs' patients. The use of immersive technology has assisted Med Learning Group in delivering engaging content that resonates with its audience. From the Igloo perspective, there are several key factors that contribute to the organisation's success.

Commitment to content creation

Med Learning Group has been creating VR content since the early days of the medium. For each of its educational programmes, it develops unique content in-house, all introduced by experts in the field, which immerses participants in detailed visualisations. With its background in VR content, Med Learning Group has a deep understanding of how to make outstanding content for its VR Rooms.

Making the most of the branding options

One of the benefits of an Igloo portable structure is that it has a blank canvas for branding. Med Learning Group creates custom covers for its VR Rooms at each event, stamping the rooms with its own identity. By creating such eye-catching showpieces, Med Learning Group ensures that participants are drawn into the space and content.

A disciplined approach to evaluation and optimisation

Med Learning Group is always looking to evaluate and optimise the effectiveness of its educational programmes. Drawing on its scientific background, it uses robust research techniques to judge knowledge acquisition, attitude change, and recall amongst its audiences. And, in a spirit of continual improvement, it feeds its findings into future programmes. By taking such a disciplined approach to measurement and evaluation, Med Learning Group ensures that it gets maximum benefit from shared immersive spaces.